LOST SOULS

A fictional journey through 50 years of PINK FLOYD

Edwin Ammerlaan

EA Media

Published February 2021 by EA Media
Amsterdam, Netherlands
www.eamedia.nl

Cover photography: Ronen Goldman
www.ronengoldman.com

ISBN 978-90-9034095-1
NUR 666

This work is based upon real events and interviews. Certain events, dialogue and characters have been created and adapted for the purposes of fictionalisation.

So build me a time
When the characters rhyme
And the story line is kind

Pink Floyd - Ibiza Bar

FOREWORD

A few years ago, a local publisher asked me if I would be interested in writing a biography about Pink Floyd. I've been a freelance music journalist since 1987 and have written many features about Pink Floyd in that time. To be asked to work on a book about such an iconic band meant that, by a few people at least, I was considered to be an 'expert'. I felt honoured but declined. The reason I turned the proposition down had nothing to do with the fee I was being offered, nor with the projected six to eight months of hard, dedicated work. I rejected it because I felt that most things about Pink Floyd had already been thoroughly documented. To add a new perspective would be virtually impossible.

The offer did get me thinking, though. I've always been fascinated by Pink Floyd's music, the odd combination of egos involved and the intriguing, weird, wonderful, innovative, confronting, soulful, and monumental songs they created. A book about how they found and lost each other in pursuit of the one common goal of becoming a success? Now that would be an interesting challenge!

Writing an in-depth-non-biographical-behind-the-scenes essay on the inner workings of Pink Floyd seemed like a daunting task. Apart from Nick Mason's Inside Out autobiography - a great read, by the way -, Nick Sedgwick's In The Pink (Not A Hunting Memoir) and the handful of interviews that dared to venture into the band's psyche, there's not much written about what went on behind the

Floydian wall of silence. Sure, the music press seized the many opportunities whenever things between messieurs Gilmour and Waters got a little out of hand, but most of those features simply recycled the same quotes and anecdotes. We learned nothing more than that both men disliked each other for the way the other dealt with the heritage of the b(r)and name.

I had to think of a new concept. A concept, now aiming at an international audience, which would allow me to look at Pink Floyd from a more personal, subjective perspective. I decided to base my book on real-life events from the band's history, but also to add some 'made-up' stories along the way (like playing a round of golf with Roger Waters). I also introduced a fictional principal character, Matt, so I could (re)visit events and comment on the band's history as it unfolded. By placing these events in chronological order and having Matt present at them all, I realised my book was also becoming a kind of coming-of-age story. At this point I incorporated some of my personal experiences of working and growing up in the music industry as well.

Because I now had fictional characters meeting real people, my next challenge was to make sure the dialogue between them was not too far-fetched. For that I needed to come up with quotes that were as close to the 'imaginary truth' as possible. Enter many months of research. I collected hundreds of quotes from multiple sources including interviews - some of which I'd done myself -, books, DVD's, and YouTube-clips. (You'll find a full list in the bibliography section.) When it came to writing the book, I transformed many of the quotes I'd amassed into conversational exchanges that fitted the time, place and people involved. Other quotes I completely rewrote and, inevitably, some dialogue I just had to make up on the spot.

I realise that I was extremely fortunate to cherry pick from such a rich tree of resources and I can't stress enough how grateful I am to all the journalists who in one form or another have contributed to this story - thank you!

Even though Lost Souls is largely based on real events and interviews, the main storyline is a work of fiction: a novel written from a journalist's perspective with information accumulated through some serious research, but with which I have taken huge liberties as I made it fictional. Or factional, if you please. Above of all, it is a book written with love and passion for the music of Pink Floyd and with the deepest respect and admiration for the band members, their crew, families, and all the people involved.

Edwin Ammerlaan
Amsterdam
February 2021

67
ECHOES

Berkeley Hotel, London, July 5, 2017

"Actually, Matt, I don't give a fuck what you think."

His words reverberated through the old Victorian hotel room like gunshots in a cathedral. The look in his eyes was the coldest I had ever seen.

Stunned and unable to comprehend what had just happened, I desperately tried to think of a suitable retort. I'd been hurt by a long-time friend and he obviously didn't care. Admittedly, we'd had our share of disagreements over the past fifty years, but they'd always been quickly dispelled with a handshake or a joke. Not today. Today was different.

Had I been too blunt in my observations? Had I underestimated how sensitive the issue was? I had no idea. I took a few deep breaths and as my confusion slowly faded, anger took over.

"Well, I think you're an ass, too!" I heard myself blurt out.

Instantly, Roger Waters' face softened and with a curious mix of affection and pity, he slowly raised himself up out of the chair and walked towards the door. As he passed behind me, I felt him pat my shoulder with his hand, exactly as he'd done fifty years ago on the day we first met.

"I think 'pain in the ass' is the expression you're looking for," Waters said as he left the room. "A pain in the ass. And proud of it!"

17

BIKE

Ibiza & Formentera, August 1967

Uncertain whether the assistant considered me a daredevil or just plain batty, I wheeled the rental bike out of the shop and rode to the hostel to pick up my stuff. I was planning on spending the next couple of days on the island of Formentera, and a bike would be much more convenient than ambling about on foot.

I whizzed through the narrow streets at breakneck speed, indifferent to the short steep climbs, brutal descents, and the spattering of Spanish curses along the way. It was clear the local people were not used to seeing a fearless young tourist hurtle his bike over pedestrian walkways. When some refused to let Flash-Gordon-on-two-wheels pass, it took some spectacular breaking and skilful steering to avoid a couple of head-on collisions. With last month's TV footage of Tom Simpson's tragic death on the slopes of Mont Ventoux still fresh in mind, I slowed the Tour-de-Ibiza down until I reached the hostel where my rucksack lay waiting patiently next to the front desk.

A few handshakes and 'adíosses' later, I was back in the saddle. This time it was me doing the cursing. I had not expected the weight on my shoulders to unleash the rivers of sweat that were now gushing out of almost every pore of my body. I pedalled the last stretch to the ferry terminal as slowly as I could. Drenched and with the sun already burning my skin, I was glad to finally board the ship. A refreshing draught instantly cooled my overheated limbs, and I decided to stay put. When a rough-looking man told me I was blocking the way and to move on, I complied and secured my bike in the designated spot.

For such a small island, a surprisingly large number of people had booked the 30-minute trip to Formentera; the boat was buzzing with day-trippers, long-stayers and general sightseers. There were a couple of Americans, some locals, a few European tourists, and hippies. Lots of hippies. I didn't really know what to think of them. Their music seemed OK and some so-called hippie artists I liked a lot. Jimi Hendrix, Janis Joplin, Jefferson Airplane, and a few others I'd been introduced to by my older brother. It was creative, exciting new stuff. I wasn't too keen on the way they dressed, though. I couldn't see myself wearing leather vests, tie dye shirts, grungy jeans, sandals, let alone the Peace Symbol, which was pretty much a hippie fashion essential.

Since most passengers had made a beeline for the shade over the lower deck, I had plenty of empty chairs to choose from. As the ferry left the dock and the wind picked up, I no longer noticed the sun's rays on my skin.

It didn't take long before people returned to the upper deck. Some went straight to the railings to watch Ibiza recede into the distance, others settled down on a chair. One rather exotic and bohemian-looking group came over to where I was sitting and plonked themselves down onto the hot metal floor in front of my chair. The cheerful, laid-back mood of the party mesmerised me. Most were in their early twenties and some were smoking what looked like giant cigarettes.

One guy with long curly black hair and dark eyes stood out like there was a bulb above his head. When someone handed the charismatic man a guitar, the others eagerly gathered around.

For a while, he just sat there with the instrument resting in his lap, smoking and chatting in a soft, dreamy voice, but I couldn't hear what he was saying. It must have been a fascinating story because everyone listened enthralled. He had the natural charisma of a bright young film star, and I imagined he was telling tales of his travels and the amazing people he had met along the way; how he'd gone boozing and gambling with Jack Kerouac in San Francisco, written poetry with Serge Gainsbourg in Paris or met Brigitte Bardot on the beaches of St. Tropez.

Slowly, my eyes drifted over to one of the three girls in the group. She was without doubt the prettiest of them all. With long blond hair wafting in the sea breeze, sparkling green eyes and Mona Lisa smile, she had a distant air as if she was on a different planet. Or a different ferry. Sailing from Ibiza to Nirvana.

Enjoying the view, I continued to gaze unnoticed for another couple of glorious minutes until, suddenly, I felt the pat of a hand on my shoulder.

"She's way out of your league, man," a voice whispered from behind. Taken by surprise, my heart skipped a few beats and, blushing, I turned to see a tall man in his mid-twenties looking down on me with a somewhat cruel, yet disarming smile.

"Hi, I'm Roger," he said, holding two cans of lager in his left hand.

I was too startled to speak.

"And that's Syd and a few of our friends," he added, nodding at the guitarist.

Roger walked over to the guy he'd said was called Syd, handed him one of the beers, returned and dropped onto the empty chair beside me.

"Don't mind if I sit here, do you?" he asked with a slightly posh British accent.

"No, not at all. I'm Matt," I replied and shook his hand.

Roger had a long pale face with high cheekbones and piercing, grey-green eyes that were half-hidden by a mane of dark brown hair. Dressed in jeans and in an unbuttoned, long-sleeved black shirt, he didn't look like your average British tourist.

"Are you guys hippies?" I asked, regretting the question almost the moment it left my mouth.

"Good God, no!" he replied, still grinning.

"Fuckin' hate hippies. Lazy bunch of wankers if you ask me. My friends Syd, Rick, and I are musicians. We're taking a break for a few days of to get ourselves some sunshine."

Syd had started playing his guitar. Waterloo Sunset, if I was not mistaken. He was softly humming the words with some of the group singing along.

"Is she your girlfriend?," I asked, pointing at the girl with the rippling blond hair. "Or Syd's?"

Roger shook his head. "Nah, she's one the girls we met in Ibiza. She's a beauty, isn't she? We call her the Queen of Spain. Premier league, if you know what I mean. No use in trying. I think she fancies Syd."

"Does he fancy her back?"

"With Syd, you never can tell. He makes up his own rules and they change from day to day. Some girls are attracted by that, Matt, although most of them just find it confusing. I think our Spanish queen will need an armada, not just a ferry to conquer his heart."

Syd switched from the Kinks to The Beatles, but after a few chords of Penny Lane got bored and changed to a song I didn't know. Something about a cat and a witch. It sounded like a catchy tune. Then he looked bored again and stopped playing altogether. The group carried on talking. And smoking.

"I think I'll join my friends, if you don't mind," Roger excused himself. "Nice meeting you, Matt," he added, jumping up and dropping onto the floor right next to the Spanish royalty.

Even though I was sitting ten feet away from them, I suddenly felt I was crashing a private party. Besides, I was starting to notice the sun's blistering effect on my skin. I got up, went inside, walked straight up to the bar, and ordered a beer. At home, I had two suspicious parents lurking around almost every domestic corner, so except for the odd party with buddies from school, my life up to this moment had mostly been alcohol-free. Here, on my first ever solo holiday adventure, drinking cervezas was exhilarating and it made me feel mature. Seventeen, but no questions asked.

Shortly after arriving at our destination, I walked back to the car deck to pick up my bike. I saw Roger and his friends waiting near the passenger exit.

"See ya!" I called over with a wave.

"Have fun, Matt," Roger called back.

"Nice bike, man!" Syd added.

▪ ▪ ▪

Stretching eleven miles from one end to the other, Formentera is the smallest of the inhabited Balearic Islands and has no airport and only a few paved roads. To me, it looked like a piece of brownish rock sticking out of the azure sea. In Ibiza, some friendly natives had advised me to follow the road into Sant Ferran de Ses Roques where I would find a restaurant and bar called La Fonda Pepe, a hostel, a bakery and a few houses. Sant Ferran seemed like a good place to be for my two days of sight-seeing. Luckily, the hostel had a bed to spare for a reasonable rate. Check-in was swift and painless, so after dropping my gear, I went looking for the one thing left on my mind: another cold, refreshing beer.

It was late in the afternoon and, with the cool sea breeze gone, relaxing out on the terrace seemed the sensible thing to do. It was busy outside the café. People were standing around talking or sitting, reading a book or newspaper. One man on the corner was writing notes, looking quite intellectual and preoccupied. I found a table with a couple of free chairs, and sat down, unsure of what to do or what to expect next. Nobody paid any attention to me or my beer, as if I was already part of the regular clientele. The cheerful sound of Scott McKenzie's San Francisco wafted out of the pub's open windows, followed by The Spencer Davis Group's I'm A Man. A perfect soundtrack to a perfect day.

"Hello, bicycle boy," I heard a timid voice next to me say.

I looked up to see Syd from the ferry smiling down at me. These guys continued to surprise the hell out of me.

"Hey, hello!" I said and held out my hand. "I'm Matt."

"Roger," he replied quietly, "Roger Barrett. My friends call me Syd."

"Cool place, isn't it?" I said.

"Yeah," Syd answered. "Good vibe. I like the music too."

"Is Roger, your friend I met on the ferry here too?" I asked out of curiosity.

"No, he's here visiting friends for the day. He's going back to Ibiza tonight."

There was something about this guy I found intriguing, although I couldn't quite figure out what it was. His face was pale and he looked kind of tired, but from under his black curly hair his eyes sparkled with an enchanting mixture of mischief and mystery. No wonder the girls on the ferry were drawn to him.

"Roger said you play in a band together."

"Yeah, we're called The Pink Floyd. We've just finished touring the UK. It's been pretty busy."

"The Pink Floyd...," I repeated, adding apologetically: "Doesn't ring a bell, I'm afraid."

"No worries, man. We've only had one single out so far. But I'm not really into all that. Bringing out singles or being famous doesn't do much for me, I just want to write and play my songs."

"What kind of music do you make, Syd?"

"We play songs for people to dance to. They don't seem to dance much now, but that was the initial idea. We play loud and we mess around with electric guitars using all the volume and the effects we can get. Right now, we're trying to develop this show using lots of lights..."

"Sounds interesting," I replied. "Have you released any LP's, yet?"

"Yes, in fact we have. Our first album was released just a few weeks ago. But hey man," Syd said, abruptly standing up, "I've got to split. Come and look us up when we're playing sometime. Bye-bye, bike boy." And off he went.

A girl I'd not noticed before was standing on the street just a few yards from the terrace, smiling and waving wildly at him. I watched as he went to meet her. When they'd disappeared, I stood up and walked over to the man who was still writing away on the corner.

"Excuse me, I'm sorry to disturb you, but could I borrow your pen for a second?"

Without looking up or saying a word, he lifted his hand and offered me his pen. I picked up a beermat from an adjoining table and wrote three words on it: The Pink Floyd.

Back at the hostel, my sunburn and a massive thunderstorm kept me awake half the night. The next day I decided I should take it easy: a bit of sightseeing, a swim and, hopefully, a kip on the beach would be just fine. I asked the landlady for a large towel, wrapped it around my neck, filled an empty bottle with water and got on my bike.

I headed for the market at El Pilar de La Mola and followed the paths to the eastern tip of the island, in search of good sea views and a beach. The dusty roads wove through a barren moonscape, but I was enjoying my little touristic trip. And with almost no traffic to watch out for, my thoughts drifted back to my encounters with the two Rogers. Syd was obviously a dreamer: a charming, romantic, and creative poet-type. The other Roger was more of an outspoken and energetic go-getter; not someone you want to mess with. I wondered how their music sounded and what it would be like to play in a loud band. I smiled, realising I didn't even know what instruments they played. Noisy electric guitars, most likely. The Pink Floyd... I reminded myself not to forget that beermat when I return home.

▪ ▪ ▪

Thanks to last night's thunderstorm, the temperature was not as relentless as yesterday. I stretched out on the white sand and I closed my eyes. By the time I opened them again, a good hour had gone. After a quick swim to get the juices flowing, I was all geared up for some more sightseeing.

As I coasted towards the island's small capital of Sant Francesc Xavier, there was plenty of time to take in the breathtaking scenery. I promised myself I would return to Formentera. Maybe I would buy a house here, write a book, take up painting or, who knows, even write some music of my own. To be a successful artist and live on a sunny island. Wouldn't that be something.

I continued my reverie until, reaching the outskirts of the little town, I suddenly saw a familiar figure standing a hundred yards off to the side of the road. Hitting the brakes, I gaped in disbelief at the strangely disturbing scene. There, in front of two whitewashed windmills, was the unmistakable figure of Syd Barrett. Motionless, he was staring up at the rotating wooden sails. But that was not what bothered me. It was more about the way he was standing there, perfectly still with his arms stretched out to the sides. With his long dark hair and a white, long-sleeved linen t-shirt hanging loosely over his shorts, he looked like Jesus. Like a human cross in the desolate field of his promised island.

Something was definitely amiss. Not wanting to crash in on him, I got off my bike and wheeling it beside me, approached him on foot. I'd got to about ten yards from where he was standing when he abruptly lowered his arms and hugged them tightly to his body.

"Syd, it's me, Matt. Are you alright?" I asked, with concern in my voice.

Barrett stared at me blankly but didn't reply.

The sparkle in his eyes was gone. I wasn't even sure he was seeing me at all.

"Is there anything I can do for you? Would you like some water?"

Nothing.

I took the bottle from the bike and was just starting to move forward to give it to him, when he suddenly turned around and walked away. I watched in disbelief as he strode with a firm step in the direction of the town where the setting sun was disappearing behind a row of white houses. I was too dumbfounded to do anything, nor did I realise I would never see The Pink Floyd's Syd Barrett, again.

18
KEEP SMILING PEOPLE

Amsterdam, Netherlands, May 23, 1968

Now it was there right in front of me, I was having a hard time understanding what all the fuss was about. Sure, it was huge, but so were some Frans Hals, Govert Flinck and Bartholomeus van der Helst militia pieces I'd seen hanging in Amsterdam's Rijksmuseum.

Apparently, they paid Rembrandt 1600 guilders to paint his Night Watch in 1642. It was just one of many group portraits commissioned by the Civil Guard, and originally hung next to several similar paintings in the militia's Assembly Hall. What is it that makes this one so special, I wondered? In fact, why is the Night Watch still considered one of the most important paintings in the world? And, now that I'm thinking about it, why would anyone studying journalism want to write a review of a 300-year-old canvas in the first place? Surely this city has a lot more to offer than some relics from the past.

It wasn't that I disliked the Night Watch particularly, I was just feeling fed up and restless at being in a museum. I'd never been to Amsterdam before and like most first-time visitors, I was more drawn by the cool, laid-back atmosphere in the centre of this gorgeous city. I wanted to be outside seeing more of the canals, the Vondelpark, shops, bars, and cafes.

Reluctantly, I opened my notebook and wrote: 'Captain Frans Banninck Cocq is giving orders. Lieutenant Willem van Ruytenburch is wearing yellow and blue - probably the colours of his militia. Painting called Night Watch because years of dirt and layers of varnish made it darker than it originally was. Led to misconception that the militia were patrolling at night. Men all wearing hats, most have a beard, a moustache or both. R painted some faces with a fine eye for detail, others more quickly and vague. Can't explain why the little girl is placed so prominently in the centre. And why is a bird (chicken?) hanging upside down by its claws from the waistband of her dress? A symbolic message? Amusing little detail: on the back row, slightly above and to the left of the captain's hat, a man is peeking over the shoulders of two distinguished looking noblemen. Hidden from the rest, you can only see a part of his head. Made me laugh. Doesn't need to be in there. Is it meant to be a joke? Rembrandt must have been a funny guy.'

It may not be my favourite painting, but it did have a story to tell. I now had plenty to write about, although I should probably look Rembrandt van Rijn up in the library before starting my essay when I'm home. I closed the notebook and looked at my watch. I was due to meet the rest of my class at Anne Frank's house on the Prinsengracht for our group assignment at three. I still had plenty of time to enjoy a Heineken or two. Time to go.

Leaving the museum, I crossed the busy Stadhouderskade, turned left onto the Weteringschans and walked towards the Leidseplein, one of Amsterdam's liveliest squares. Just before hitting the plaza, its pavement cafes already in sight, my eyes caught on a big colourful poster stuck on the window of an old three-storey brick building. I instantly recognised the handwritten words: The Pink Floyd. Hey, I know these guys! I felt as excited as I had a couple of months earlier when I'd finally heard See Emily Play on the radio and my mind had shot back to meeting Roger and Syd the previous summer.

Hearing the band's single had also been quite a revelation: so that was the kind of music they played! It was a nice little tune with mysterious lyrics and a catchy chorus. The spacey sounds and weird twists were like nothing I'd ever heard before, and the song stuck in my head for weeks. I had intended to check out their other music, but completely forgot and, eventually, the band had slipped out of my mind. Until now.

The poster had today's date written on it and 'Paradiso', which was obviously the name of the place. There was no mention of a time. Would Roger and Syd still remember me? I had to find out. The front door was firmly shut and, with no sign of any activity, I looked around for another way in. To my surprise, one of the two other entrances on the left side of the building was unlocked. I opened it carefully and peered inside at what looked to be some kind of church. Balanced on top of rows of pillars, an ornate balcony ran around three sides of the main hall and looked down onto a stage framed by some enormous stained-glass windows. There was even a full-blown organ high above the main entrance doors. The stage was empty and there was absolutely nothing to suggest that The Pink Floyd was going to be performing there any time soon. Weird.

I was about to leave when a grumpy-looking guy wearing jeans, a Lucky Strike sweater and a red bandana walked in. Surprised to see me, he raised his hand either in greeting or to warn me not to go any further. I wasn't sure which.

"Hey there, can I help you?"

"Em, actually," I replied, hesitantly, "I'm looking for

Roger. He's with The Pink Floyd. We're friends. Obviously, he's not here yet."

My bluff seemed to work, though the guy remained his grumpy self.

"No man. You should come back later. They're doing a gig somewhere else. Not expecting them 'till late. Show starts at ten."

"Oh, I see. Thanks. See you later."

I turned around and left the Paradiso. My mind was made up. Come what may, I was going to be at the concert tonight.

▪ ▪ ▪

Brown was the dominant colour in café Reijnders. I guess the Dutch don't call it a brown café for nothing. It was the first decent pub I'd come to on the Leidseplein, and I decided to skip Anne Frank's house right there and then. I wouldn't make in it time anyway and I couldn't have cared less. I was dying to see The Pink Floyd. What would they sound like live? Would I get to talk to them again? I just needed to kill four hours before the Paradiso opened its doors.

I sat down, ready to order. Opposite me, four students in their early twenties were sitting silently doing nothing, all looking bored to tears as they scrutinised the clientele. I made eye contact with one of the girls: a brunette with bright green eyes, a long ponytail, white painted nails and flowers sewn on her jeans. She returned my look with a nice, warm smile.

"Hi! Do any of you know the Paradiso?" I asked.

Three of them were off in their own little worlds and ignored me, but the brunette with the ponytail moved her chair a little closer to mine.

"Not yet, it only opened this March," she replied with a cute Dutch accent. "Why are you asking?"

"I'm planning on going there tonight," I replied.

The conversation fell silent, but luckily the waiter arrived. I ordered a beer. The girl who was now sitting next to me asked for a Coke. The other girls suddenly also got up, joined my table and ordered drinks too.

"Are you a tourist?" the brunette asked. The other three now perked up and listened eagerly.

"No, I'm a student doing an assignment for my art class. I've just been to the Rijksmuseum. The rest of my class is at the Anne Frank house."

"And you're not," one of the other girls remarked, clearly in a moment of heightened observation.

"Why not?"

"It's not compulsory," I answered in defence mode. "As long as I'm back at the youth hostel by eleven. We're going back home tomorrow. With the bus."

I wasn't sure why I thought I needed to share this extra information, but I seemed to still have their attention.

"But what are you doing here?" The girl persisted.

"I'm fed up with the assignments, I guess. And I want to see The Pink Floyd play in the Paradiso, tonight."

The waiter brought our drinks. Out of the blue, my brunette then turned to me and asked: "Can I come too?"

Her friends looked puzzled. I was too.

"Sure, that'd be fun."

"Yeah! We'll all go!" Another of the other girls shrieked with excitement. People in the pub turned their heads.

"Yeah! Let's all go see Jim Boyd," she yelled again.

"Pink Floyd..." I corrected.

I leaned over the brunette and asked: "What's your name?"

"Carly," she whispered back.

I smiled.

"Hi Carly, I'm Matt."

Carly and I spent the rest of the afternoon and early evening chatting and eating burgers. We talked about our schools, the places we lived, our families and music. She turned out to be 20 and living with her mum in a town near Amsterdam, called Amstelveen. Her father had died of alcohol poisoning when she was nine. She and her friends were having a few days off from university. She was studying history. As did her friends.

I paid for all the drinks and burgers, even though I'd hardly talked to the other three. They didn't seem too bothered about it though; after a free meal and drinks, they were looking forward to a wild night with Jim Boyd.

▪▪▪

It must have been around 8:30 pm when the five of us arrived at the Paradiso. The doors were open and as there was no queue, we walked up the steps to a little booth on the left where I paid five guilders for two tickets. The other girls hadn't expected to pay for themselves and were clearly bugged by my sudden lack of generosity.

Inside the dark venue, people were sitting, standing, and just lying around. There was a lot of smoking going on. I wasn't sure I liked the smell of pot. Carly didn't complain, although the others looked a bit out of their comfort zone. We found ourselves one of the Persian rugs. Getting as close as I could to my cute Dutch brunette, we sat back and took in the relaxed, laid back groove.

Carly's friends quickly got bored and after a while they stood up and began wandering around until they'd disappeared altogether. Had they left the building? I cared little, I was sitting next to a girl I had grown fond of and I was enjoying our chats. We talked about the student protests and riots in Paris and about the Vietnam War, which she strongly opposed. Since Rotterdam was hosting the European Cup finals tonight we even chatted a bit about football. After a while, the Paradiso got a lot busier and we had to stand up. I estimated there were around a thousand people inside; most of them stoned out of their minds.

The house lights dimmed, the spotlights took over and The Pink Floyd walked onto the stage. I immediately recognised Roger Waters and the keyboard player from the ferry but Syd, the other Roger, wasn't with them, just some other guitarist and a drummer with a funny-looking moustache.

Nothing could have prepared me for what happened next. Waters mumbled a few words to the audience, and then the band began to play. And man, they played LOUD! The music was a raw, sometimes chaotic mix of pulsating beats, soaring electric guitar and psychedelic organ whirls. Mostly, it sounded unstructured and aggressive, with only a few brief, reflective interludes. It wasn't anything like the See Emily Play single I'd heard on the radio. And it certainly wasn't close to what I'd expected to hear from those nice blokes I'd met on the Ibiza ferry.

Shocked by the intensity of the racket, it took a while before I could settle down and really listen. I didn't know what to make of it, whether I liked the music or not. Carly looked appalled. I saw her put her hands over her ears trying to block out the noise and when bright white stroboscopic lights started flashing, she covered her eyes. After about twenty minutes, she grabbed me by the shoulders, pulled me towards her and shouted: "I want to leave. Can we go, please?"

I desperately wanted to see the rest of the concert, but I didn't want to upset Carly either. Taking her hand, I guided her towards the doors that separated the venue from the quiet entrance area. Once we'd made it outside, I turned and saw she was crying.

"I'm sorry, Matt," she sniffled, "It's too loud and I don't like the music. But I don't want to spoil your evening."

For a moment, we just stood there. Me looking at the exit, Carly facing the floor. I didn't know what to say and suggested a bit of a weak compromise: "Do you want to meet up after the concert?"

"Dunno," she whispered, wiping away a tear with the back of her hand.

"Why not?"

"You're leaving tomorrow anyway..."

"We can still spend some time together tonight," I pleaded. "We could even meet tomorrow morning if you like. Grab a coffee and..."

"...dunno," she said again.

I felt awkward and didn't know what to say. The music from behind the doors was calling me back in, but my hormones were telling me otherwise. After a few more seconds of avoided eye contact, Carly suddenly kissed me on the cheek.

"Was great meeting you, Matt."

She turned around and walked out through the door.

My Amsterdam girl was gone. I'd not even taken her address or phone number, and now I'd never see her again. What an idiot! Fighting back one or two of my own tears, I went back to join the crowd.

The Pink Floyd was playing as relentlessly as before and I was brought to myself with a bang. Then, right in the middle of a song, the keyboards fell silent. Nobody panicked. The musicians just stood there, perfectly calm and a little bemused, as a few guys came on stage and studied the floor with a torch. I noticed a photographer in the back scuttle away. After 20 seconds at most, one of the crew gave the thumbs up and the band started to play again, picking up where they'd left off as if nothing had happened.

The show continued for another thirty minutes. The house lights came on and it was all over. Most people headed straight for the doors, some hung around while others, unbelievably, lay sleeping on the floor. I even noticed a group of people dancing even though there was no music to dance to.

Musing over what I'd just seen, I walked over to the bar. In terms of sheer energy, The Pink Floyd had put on an incredible performance. Their music was kind of mind-boggling, in a sort of unfathomable way. I still wasn't sure if I'd liked the songs, but they'd taken me to places I'd never been before. And I was probably the only person there unable to attribute his trip to smoking grass.

I ordered a beer, emptied the glass in one go and walked towards the exit. On my way out, I saw a sign for the toilets pointing down towards a large wooden staircase. I followed the signs, found the bathrooms, and took a leak. On my way back to the stairs, I saw some people walking towards the other end of the basement. I followed them, hoping to find the dressing rooms. Maybe I could sneak in and exchange a quick 'hello' with Roger and the other band members.

We entered a short, narrow hallway leading up to a closed door and when the people in front of me stopped, so did I. We stood there patiently waiting for a while, then the door opened and the guy with the red bandana ushered us in. I took a quick look around and noticing the keyboard player sitting quietly in one of the small dressing rooms, I walked over and introduced myself.

"Hi, I'm Matt. Thanks for a great show. It was loud but

brilliant," I said.

He smiled.

"Thanks. We had a lot of technical issues, but it was OK. We like playing here."

He spoke with a gentle voice.

"The power failure? What happened?"

"Oh, some photographer tripped over a cable. Not a very clever thing to do on stage. That thing with Roger was much more concerning."

I gave him a puzzled look.

"He almost electrocuted himself," the keyboard player explained, no longer smiling. "Wrong cables or wrong voltage. Either way, it was pretty scary."

Right on cue, I heard a familiar voice say: "Hey you!"

I looked to the left and saw Roger grinning at me. "Ibiza ferry, right? How are you, man?"

Delighted he still remembered me, I shook his hand.

"Doing very well, sir! Thank you. That was a great show, tonight. Glad you're still alive!"

"An occupational hazard. Comes with the job. Nothing to worry about. Did you have a great time on Formentera?"

"I sure did. I met Syd again," I said, not going into the specifics. "Why isn't he here playing with you?"

"I'm afraid we had to let him go," Roger replied.

"Oh, why's that?"

Roger paused, sizing me up.

"What was your name again?"

"Matt."

"Ah, yes, I remember now. Well, you see Matt, Syd isn't his usual self lately, and he can't play anymore. We want to move forward, but with Syd in the band we never know where we're at. Some things simply had to change."

The keyboard player looked sad. Roger didn't seem all that bothered.

“What happened?” I asked.

“One trip too many. Or too many trips too many. I don’t know. It’s not something we’re proud of, but he couldn’t handle it anymore. Maybe he’ll sober up and come back. I’m not sure.”

“That’s a pity, I liked the guy.”

“Yeah, I do too. We all do. We go back a long time. We’re still friends. Hopefully, he’ll come to his senses.”

The room felt silent. The keyboard player had already left to talk to some other people.

“What do you think of David?” Roger suddenly asked.

“David?”

“Our new guy on guitar.”

“Well, at least you now have somebody who knows how to play his instrument,” I replied.

“Cheeky little bastard, aren’t you?” Roger laughed. “Follow me, I’ll see if I can find him.”

Roger led me through the small corridor, checking the crowded rooms. In one of them, somebody he knew and hadn’t seen in a long time called out to him. The two men hugged and started an animated conversation. After a few seconds, he turned his head and, realising I was waiting, apologised and dismissed me: “Sorry, mate, no idea where he is. Talk to you later, right?”

“Sure, no problem, Roger.”

Not knowing what to do next, I followed a set of stairs leading up to the stage. The roadies were still busy removing instruments and gear. Not wanting to be in their way, I quickly jumped off the stage and walked towards the open doors at the side of the venue. Outside, the crew were loading some cases into an old black Ford Transit. The petrol cap had obviously gone missing and someone had replaced it with a bunch of newspaper.

Next to the van, the guitarist was sitting on top of a case, smoking a cigarette.

"Better be careful," I said, smiling and pointing at the newspapers, "you don't want to set those on fire."

"Yeah, that'd be the shortest band career ever. Say goodbye with a bang," he replied. "And then they'll have to look for another guitar player all over again."

"Hi, I'm Matt."

"David."

"Did you enjoy tonight?" I asked.

"Yes, pretty much so. Glad so many people came out to see us. Always more fun than playing in front of only a handful, you know? There were some technical hiccups, but we all thought it was a decent gig. And you?"

"I thought it was great! It was really intense, especially with those flashing lights. I met some of the guys in Ibiza last summer. It was great to finally see them play. Shame they don't play your music on the radio much."

"We're working on that," David Gilmour explained. "We have a new manager now and he wants us to start working on a new album soon."

"Have you played in any other bands?"

"A couple. Not very successful. We mainly did covers, some bluesy stuff and vocal harmonies. Nothing like The Pink Floyd."

"I really dig your sound. It's great!"

"Thanks," David said, lighting another cigarette. "Having a great sound makes playing a lot more fun."

"Do you improvise as well?"

"Sure, to an extent. I enjoy improvising and like to mess around with lots of different effects. None of us are technically brilliant musicians, as you might have noticed. And we're not terribly good at complicated chord structures, either. A lot of it is simple stuff dressed up."

"Well, the way you dress it up is pretty cool."

We both laughed. A guy wearing a hefty pair of glasses signalled David. I looked over to see the rest of the band carrying bags of all shapes and sizes to the van.

"Sorry, got to go. We're playing a gig near Birmingham, tomorrow. Long night of travelling ahead."

"Good to meet you, David."

"Likewise, come and look us up again if you get the chance."

We shook hands again, then he grabbed his bag, tossed it into the back of the van and took his seat. I briefly caught Roger Waters' eye, waved him goodbye and immediately felt silly. Not a very rock 'n' roll thing to do. He smiled back. The van drove off, leaving me standing next to Paradiso's now deserted parking lot in the dark.

I felt exhausted but larger than life. I'd had a glorious night with glorious music and talked to some friendly, pretty awesome but down-to-earth musicians. I couldn't wait for my next rock show. The reality of the chilly night kicked in as I realised I somehow had to get back to the Youth Hostel and sneak in unnoticed. As I walked back through the quiet Amsterdam streets, I thought of Carly again. Shame she wasn't with me. I was missing her already. But, hey, I'm now friends with The Pink Floyd. Either way, I had some amazing stories to tell back home.

20

THE GATES OF DAWN

Charlton Park, Bishopsbourne, Kent, August 31st, 1970

"Just wait here. I'll come and get you in about an hour," the manager with the hefty glasses said.

Wooden picnic tables were arranged all over the area, so I singled one out and sat down. It wobbled a bit, but I was far less worried by the wobbliness than the dirt. Puddles of beer, empty bottles, grease, leftover food; it was one big sticky mess and I made sure not to touch anything with my hands. Watching the goings on in the backstage area was fun. The weather was brilliant and people were bathing in the sun, making out, smoking, playing Frisbee, talking, or lounging on the grass. I decided to just sit and enjoy the scenery.

I was a man on a mission. A mission I'd set out on only yesterday. Some of my friends decided last minute to go to the Isle of Wight festival and when they offered me a spare ticket, I'd taken it like a shot. A whole bunch of our heroes were playing: The Who, Emerson, Joni Mitchell, Lake and Palmer, Jethro Tull, Ten Years After, and, of course, Jimi Hendrix and the Doors. Armed with sleeping bags and tents, we'd backpacked to the festival. It was massive. I'd never seen such an immense crowd in my life and thought it was nothing less than a miracle that Sly and his Family's funky beats didn't sink the little island to the bottom of the Channel.

There were well over half a million people on the festival site, so bumping into David Gilmour was cosmically insane. It was just before the start of Hendrix's set and he was making his way with some other guy to the artist's gate. Unbelievably, he'd seen me, too, and stopped. David told me he was there to listen to the bands and hang out. Pink Floyd - they'd dropped the 'The' from their name - was booked to play at another festival in a couple of day's time.

The man with David introduced himself as Alan Timms. It turned out to be he was editor of Rock Parade, a music monthly. When he mentioned wanting to run a feature on Pink Floyd, I summoned up all my confidence and nominated myself for the job. To my delight, David confirmed I'd been with the band at the concert in Amsterdam and Timms, sufficiently impressed, handed me the assignment.

After we'd exchanged details, David promised to ask manager Steve to arrange the passes. In return, I promised to write the best ever Pink Floyd interview. Both wished me luck and said goodbye. I was clearly going to have to extend my weekend by an extra day and travel to Kent.

Although deep down I harboured the ambition of becoming a music critic, I had not told anyone. My parents were expecting me to move into professional newspaper journalism and write about politics, economics or, all else failing, maybe even about sport. But make a decent living by reviewing long-haired riffraff? Eh, no! I hadn't really started making serious long-term career plans anyway, let alone discuss them. And yet here I was, my career apparently jump-started and on a mission to interview a group of, well, chaps with very long hair. The adrenaline was already pumping through my veins.

Taking on the Rock Parade job had meant leaving my friends and the festival early. I needed to drop off my stuff, change into some clean clothes and, if I was going to look anything like a professional doing the interviews, I needed to borrow my dad's Philips portable tape recorder. I left the festival on Sunday, travelled home by public transport, and on Monday morning took a train to Canterbury and a bus to Charlton Park.

It was late afternoon when I reached the festival grounds. My earlier nerves had disappeared. Since my trip to Amsterdam, I'd bought all four Pink Floyd LP's: The Piper At The Gates Of Dawn, A Saucerful Of Secrets, More, and Ummagumma. I knew all their songs, had studied the lyrics and the album credits, and read a couple of interviews. Astronomy Domine, Interstellar Overdrive and Let There Be More Light I thought were brilliant. The shorter, lighter songs were fun, some made me laugh. Some I didn't like that much, especially the ones on More and Ummagumma. To me it felt like Pink Floyd wasn't sure what it wanted to be yet or which direction to go. I used most of the train ride writing questions in a little notebook. At least I was well-prepared.

▪ ▪ ▪

Musicians, roadies, bikers, freaks and dope-heads: the scene unfolding in the backstage area was like a wild parade of counterculture aficionados. There was some sort of confusion going on around the stage, with a film crew that looked like they'd no idea what they were doing, and roadies arguing and gesticulating as they shifted gear back and forth and moved the trucks about. Once or twice, I glimpsed a musician in the middle of all the chaos. Rod Stewart and the Faces were difficult to miss in their velvet suits, Rod in white, the others royal purple. I also spotted Mott The Hoople's Ian Hunter chatting with a few exotic looking girls.

"Ok, Matt, they're ready for you now."

I stood up and followed Steve O'Rourke over to where a couple of caravans and trailers were lined up. David Gilmour and Nick Mason were sitting and waiting for me under a large umbrella outside one cabin.

"I'll see if I can set you up with Roger, later," Steve said and left.

I said hello to David, introduced myself to Nick and grabbed a chair. After clumsily sliding a cassette tape into the recorder, I pushed the red button, opened my notebook and popped the first question.

"If I'm not mistaken, Pink Floyd laid its foundations down about six years ago. Can you take me back to those first few years?"

Both men smiled. "This kid isn't wasting any time," I could hear them thinking.

"Oh, most of us go way further back than that," David replied in his distinctively soft voice. "Roger, Syd, and I all grew up in Cambridge. Our mothers knew each other through Homerton, a nearby teacher's training college, and Roger and Syd both went to the same primary and grammar schools. I first met Roger when I was about 14. We used to hang around the art department at Cambridge Tech together and play guitars every lunchtime. Teaching each other, basically. Later in London, Roger met Nick and Rick at the Regent Street Polytechnic where they were both studying architecture. They formed a college band and recruited Syd, who was a student from Camberwell Art School."

"You guys started off playing rhythm & blues, right Nick?"

"We had three or four songs written by Syd," David put in, instead.

"The rest consisted of Rolling Stones and Bo Diddley songs, and some old bluesy tunes. The first one we did together was called Lucy Lee In Blue Tights, or something like that. We taped it as Lucy Leave, but we never released it, since we didn't exactly know which direction to follow. All we knew was that we wanted to record. And become successful. We still do. We were so very naïve at the time, and we sounded so bad!"

"You actually did some recording prior to the Piper album?"

"That's right," Nick answered. "We went into a studio for the first time near the end of 1964. A friend of Rick's who worked at a studio in West Hampstead, let us use some downtime for free. I believe we recorded I'm A King Bee, an old R&B classic, and three songs written by Syd: Double O Bo, Butterfly and Lucy Leave."

I was enjoying interviewing these guys. I'd understood right at the start of our conversation that these were not like the musicians you saw on TV. They were natural, sincere, down-to-earth men, and they were taking the time to answer my silly questions thoughtfully and openly. David was as relaxed as the night I'd met him in Amsterdam. He seemed genuinely interested in everything his band mate had to say. Nick had a boyish twinkle in his eye when he talked, his trademark moustache still drooping down either side of his upper lip. They gave no indication they were fed up with me yet, and I felt happy and relieved. So far, so good.

"So how did you come up with the name of the band?" I continued.

"We called ourselves The Tea Set at first, but we discovered soon after that another band was using that name. Syd came up with The Pink Floyd Sound. It was a combination of the first names of two blues musicians he was into: Pink Anderson and Floyd Council. It was very much Syd's idea. We're not particularly familiar with their music."

"People associate Pink Floyd more with the underground and hippie movement than with mainstream pop and R&B."

"Well," Nick continued carefully, "I admit we've played in what you might call the psychedelic scene, but we don't consider ourselves a hippie band. We're too busy for that: rehearsing, travelling to gigs, packing up, driving home."

"There's talk that Syd is taking too much acid and that that's why you no longer want him in the band."

"Is that what people are saying?"

David looked annoyed and lit a cigarette.

"I don't agree with that myself," he explained patiently. "I believe acid and stuff only act as catalysts. I think the problem is really that Syd can't handle the pressure that comes with success."

"Contrary to everything that's being said," Nick added, "it was getting harder and harder to work with Syd but we couldn't get through to him. He'd forget to appear at gigs and wasn't showing up at rehearsals. He even left the studio without warning in the middle of a radio broadcast. Syd clearly didn't want to appear in public with us and so one day Rick, Roger and I decided if Pink Floyd wanted to keep playing live, we'd have to do it without him. The thought of breaking with Syd was devastating to us. It still is, and we regret that."

"How did you get involved, David?"

"Well, Syd had invited me to come along to a recording session of See Emily Play. He was acting very strange and different from the last time I'd seen him. He kind of looked through you as if he wasn't quite there. Later, I went to see the band play at a party at the Royal College of Arts next to the Albert Hall. Nick here came up and asked me what I would say if, at some point, they asked me to join?"

"He took the bate!" Nick laughed.

"We then did five gigs together as a five-piece," David continued, "which was pretty strange."

"Who broke the news to Syd?" I asked.

"We didn't." Nick replied. "Two years ago, in February, we had a gig in Southampton. In the car on the way, someone said, 'Shall we pick Syd up?' and someone else said 'Let's not bother'. It may sound cruel to you now, but I thought Syd was just being bloody-minded. In the end, we were so fed up with him we could only see the short-term impact."

"And the first few gigs without him..."

"... went pretty well considering we'd never rehearsed together as a four-man line-up with David covering both the vocal and guitar parts. Thankfully, the audience didn't ask for their money back. I'm confident we took the right step."

"Is the band still on speaking terms with Syd?"

"We are," Nick said.

"He's now officially no longer a member of the band?"

"I guess not, no..."

Silence. The interview came to an uncomfortable halt. For a moment, I didn't know what to ask next. The two were clearly uneasy talking about their former colleague. They weren't shedding tears over it, but the feelings of guilt and remorse were obvious. I thought it was better to let it rest for now. I heard music coming from the stage. One of the bands had started playing. Switching focus, I turned to David.

"What made you decide to become a musician?"

"Let's see," David answered, frowning. "Bill Haley's Rock Around The Clock came out when I was eight. I was a big fan of all that rock 'n' roll stuff, but I was also a fan of Leadbelly and B.B. King. I didn't start playing until I was about 14 or

15. I was trying to learn 12-string acoustic guitar like Leadbelly at the same time as I was trying to learn lead guitar like Hank Marvin and later Eric Clapton. I've never had fast fingers and I don't practise much, so I have to rely on other things like effects and fuzzboxes."

"And how do you rate yourself as a drummer, Nick?"

"Technically? Rather feeble," he laughed. "My advantage is that I'm interested in minimalism, whereas the gymnastics of drumming doesn't appeal to me one bit. I find drum solos, even when they're played by talented drummers, extremely boring. I still enjoy the bebop drummers from the fifties. Art Blakey and so on. I think one of the best percussionists ever is Thelonious Monk. The way he plays piano is like real percussion. I've always had that sort of interest. I never took lessons. I think little of my musical abilities as an individual, but together we achieve some great stuff."

"Are you happy with the way the first album worked out?"

"Yes, I am," Nick replied. "Everything went pretty smoothly. Overall, everybody was enthusiastic. Even Syd seemed relaxed."

"You based Interstellar Overdrive around a riff from Syd, but the version played live is much longer than on the album."

"That's right. It was born in a live-in-studio environment rather than on the stage. We'll often shorten the individual sections to keep the most important elements of the song."

"Personally, I like Set The Controls For The Heart Of The Sun better..."

"Well yes, it has a catchy riff too," Nick continued. "I got the chance to emulate a piece called Blue Sands by jazz drummer Chico Hamilton in Set The Controls. It's fun to play live. You'll hear it tonight and can decide for yourself. I like the title track, A Saucerful Of Secrets, as well. That was carefully constructed though. Instead of using the standard song structure, Roger and I mapped it all out in advance according to the classical music convention of three movements. We also used a Mellotron, an instrument that produces string sounds out of tape loops."

"Last year, you released Ummagumma: a part live, part studio album. Why was that? Couldn't you make your mind up?"

"Very funny. It was just a gas to make."

"Yeah, it was," David said, adding cautiously: "We decided each of us should do their own piece and try to write their own songs. I'd written nothing before and just tacked some bits and pieces together."

"I did my piece mostly in cahoots with Norman Smith," Nick said. "He was our producer and enormously helpful. I also had my wife Lindy, who's a flute player, add the woodwind. I believe Rick was the most enthusiastic of us all. He totally embraced the concept of a using a more classical approach. As I said, I honestly believe we work better as a band than as individuals."

Suddenly, a familiar voice behind me said: "Well, well, bicycle boy has now become a newspaper boy! Joining forces with the enemy, are you, Matt?"

There was a look of pity in Roger's eyes, but I didn't mind. Nick and David both stood up. "We're going to see if there's anything around here to eat," David said. "Nice talking to you again, Matt. See you after the show. Come and find us. I'm curious to know what you think of our new stuff."

Roger sat down on one of the empty chairs.

"You doing okay?" he asked.

"Yes, I am, thanks. You?"

"Not too bad, either. Although, to be honest, I've been a bit frustrated of late."

"Why's that?" I asked, flipping the cassette tape over and

pushing the Record button back down.

"Because to stay alive, we have to keep playing places and venues that are totally unsuitable. This festival, for instance. I mean, I like the park and the atmosphere and all, but somebody just told me they've only sold a thousand tickets. We agreed a fixed fee to play this gig, so we're lucky. But someone's going to lose a lot of money. We can't go on doing clubs and ballrooms like we're doing now. If we do, we'll all end up on the dole. But let's not go into that now. You've got some questions to ask."

"I was surprised to find out Pink Floyd originally played blues."

"Yeah, we played a lot of Elmore James and Willie Dixon. Everybody was into the blues at the time. Admittedly, we didn't know we had a thing going. The first three years we were professional, I made seven quid a week, not really what you'd call a living wage. Before Syd came up from Cambridge, we weren't writing our own songs. Then Syd wrote all the material. With Syd gone, the rest of us had to start doing it. I'd always been told at school that I was absolutely bloody hopeless at everything, so I had no real confidence about any of it."

"But you knew you wanted to be a musician..."

"I was always interested in guitars. I had an aunt who gave me one for my fourteenth birthday. A rather cheap, six string acoustic with metal strings. It was unbelievably painful to play, and I thought it was way too hard. After I went to college, I bought a classical guitar and taught myself to play, mostly picking it up from other people. I once took lessons from a man who lived in a big country house and kept woolly monkeys. At my second lesson, I played the little exercise he'd given me, and asked if I'd been practicing an hour a day. 'Uh, no.' When he asked if I thought I was going to and I said 'probably not,' he told me there was no point in me being there."

"And then you met Syd..."

"We went through our formative years together. We rode on my motorbike, got drunk, did a little dope, flirted with girls, all that basic stuff. Syd was our primary inspiration. Unfortunately, he's turned into a strange person. He's fucking murder to live and work with."

"What do you think happened?"

"I think Syd was more affected by his father's death than any of us realised and, after it, he kind of stepped into his father's shoes. He was quite a tyrant as a teenager at home. He has four siblings, two sisters, Rosemary and Ruth, and two brothers, Alan and Don. They're all pretty deferential towards him. At one point, things were really bad, and I phoned Alan and asked him to come to London to check Syd out. But when he arrived, Syd just pretended everything was OK. He could always twist Alan around his little finger. Alan called me up a while ago. He said: 'Thank you. Roger's had a few problems, but he's fine now.' Really? I find that hard to believe. He's planning to release another solo album later this year, but I still think he needs help."

"How does Syd's mental health affect you? It must be pretty unsettling."

"Yeah, it is," Roger said, scratching the back of his head. "I don't know what's going to come up next. It feels like we're running in circles. And I'm bored with most of the stuff we've done. You can quote me on that: I'm bored with most of the stuff we play."

"David's just said you're going to be playing some new songs tonight."

"Yeah, there is a long new piece we're doing called Atom Heart Mother. No, I'm not bored with that. But we need brass and a choir to do it right. It's weird playing it and it comes out odd, like we're all throwing clumps of clay at the wall and seeing what it looks like when it's happened. We should try to raise the standards a bit. We're always intending to, but so far, we haven't. It's a job. A fucking well-paid job if all goes right with all the ego-boosting and stuff and everything. But I think it becomes mechanical. Am I playing to spread the gospel and make people happy by playing them wonderful music? No, it's not true. I'm playing to make bread. I'm caught up in the whole pop machinery business and so are most bands."

Another silence. I had the impression Roger was trying to make a point here, although I wasn't sure what it was.

"Let's call it a day, Matt. Don't feel like talking, anyway. You don't mind, do you? Catch you after the gig."

Roger Waters got up from his chair and walked away. Guess that's it for today. Hoping I'd enough quotes to write a story, I pushed the Stop button. I still had plenty of questions left to ask, though. Confused, I picked up the tape recorder, shoved it into my bag and wandered around backstage, not sure what to do next. Everybody around me was busy doing something and, left to my own devices, I thought I might as well find myself a place to watch the rest of the programme.

▪ ▪ ▪

There was plenty of room for everybody on the thick carpet of grass. I found the perfect spot with a splendid view of the stage. The roadies were busy unplugging instruments and changing sets and I had no idea which band was up next. Neither did the people sitting next to me. One guy had just finished rolling a stack of joints and, noticing me looking at the pile, offered me one. Out of curiosity, I accepted. Before I knew it, I was happily smoking along with the rest of the crowd. This was some seriously strong weed, and it wasn't long before I needed to lie down. Using my bag as a makeshift pillow, and with the sound of some folksy band I'd never heard of floating around my head, I lay down. Basking in the late afternoon sun, I quickly dosed off.

I woke up to find my head lying flat on the grass. Darkness had fallen and Charlton Park was lit by the glow of the many little bonfires people had started. It took a few seconds to realise where I was. I had no clue what time it was, but I knew which band was playing; the haunting sounds of Set The Controls For The Heart Of The Sun filled the air. The music was coming from all around me, and I guessed it must be what the music magazines were describing as quadrophonic sound. It was amazing and a far cry from the blaring acoustics I'd heard at the Isle of Wight. Pink Floyd's stellar sound system was accompanied by a spectacular light show. I could see cameras filming the event from all angles.

The guys sitting next to me told me the band had only been playing for a couple of minutes, and, thinking I could record some of the show on the rest of the interview tape, I reached for my bag. Bag? No bag! What the hell? My bag was gone. I stood up and searched around but saw nothing that resembled it. Some dingbat must have stolen it while I was asleep, notebook, tape recorder and all. The people behind me started yelling, so I dropped back onto the grass. I wasn't worried about having to pay for a new tape deck, but felt gutted the recordings were gone, too. I also realised I'd attached my backstage pass sticker on top of my bag. Great! I wouldn't even be able to get back to see the band after the show. I touched my back pocket and sighed. At least I still had my wallet.

It took most of Careful With That Axe, Eugene for my fury to subside. So much for love, peace, and happiness. So much for trusting your fellow festival-goer. At that point, I heard Pink Floyd play the first few notes of a new song and curiosity extinguished the rest of my anger. This had to be the Atom Heart Mother piece Roger was referring to. And what a long piece it turned out to be. An instrumental jam with a mix of bluesy, jazzy patterns. On the whole, it sounded like one extended and improvised set. The band was completely engrossed in what they were doing and there wasn't much interaction with the audience. David and Roger barely raised their heads from their guitars. Nick, on the other hand, was clearly enjoying himself. With wild gestures, funny expressions, and big smiles he was trying to make eye contact with his bandmates to keep everything in sync. With his unique, expressive style of playing - elbows close to his upper body, drumming mainly with his lower arms - it was as if Nick was almost begging his fellow musicians to have some fun on stage. But most of the time, Pink Floyd looked awfully serious and focussed. Now and then, Roger mumbled something to the audience, but Richard and David seemed like they were on a different planet. With the long, laid-back, and smooth licks of Atom Heart Mother, I was finding it difficult to stay with the music. I wasn't even sure if I liked Atom Heart Mother that much.

The band got a somewhat lukewarm applause and left the stage. No encore. End of show. Pity. It was well after midnight, so most people were already on their way out. Others stuck to their bonfires, probably intending to stay the night. I walked back towards the backstage entrance. To my surprise, nobody bothered checking for passes, so I walked straight through. I wasn't the only one who profited from the lack of security; the area was swarming with people talking, laughing, playing music. I saw Roger and David were already caught up in conversation. Nick was nowhere to be seen. I walked up to Richard who was sitting on a chair under a big oak tree smoking a cigarette. We shook hands, but I wasn't sure if he remembered me.

"Great show, Rick. Liked the new stuff," I lied.

"Thanks."

"I'm Matt. We met briefly at the Paradiso gig in Amsterdam two years ago."

"Oh, yes. I thought you looked familiar. What brings you up here, Matt?"

"Work," I said, trying to smile. "I'm writing a piece for Rock Parade. I did some interviews with the other guys earlier today."

"OK. Cool. Any scoops?"

"I wish..."

"You don't seem particularly happy with the result," Richard observed.

"Somebody stole my recorder with the tape still in it. My interviews are all gone..."

"Oh, that sucks. But, hey, come back anytime. We'll give it another try."

"Thanks. Not sure what I'm going to tell the editor, though..."

"Tell him we want you back to cover the rest of the story. Back by popular demand."

Before I could think of a suitable reply, a woman with long brown hair and a friendly smile joined the conversation.

"Darling, there are some people I want you to meet," she said.

"Matt, meet Juliette, my wife. Juliette, meet Matt, future star reporter of Rock Parade."

"Hi, Juliette!"

"Hello, Matt. Sorry to rob this gentleman away from you. We have guests to entertain."

"No problem, I was about to leave, anyway. I've a night

train to catch," I lied, again.

"See you later," Richard said and, putting his arm around Juliette's shoulders, he left.

For a second, I considered looking up the other guys, but I felt too tired and disappointed. Robbed of my bag and of the illusion that Pink Floyd's new music would take the world by storm. I grabbed a bottle of beer from a big ice filled bucket and walked towards the exit. Now, let's find me a night train to catch.

20
IF

Release of Atom Heart Mother, October 2, 1970

Pink Floyd
Atom Heart Mother

If Ummagumma showcased a Pink Floyd adrift without direction, Atom Heart Mother serves as a testament the band is still at a complete loss on how to move forward stylistically. Although they've largely left the aimless psychedelic experimentation behind them, the new album is as bereft of interesting melodic themes, clever lyrics and a clear musical strategy as the last. The entire first side of the record is taken up by the Atom Heart Mother Suite, a 24 minutes long orchestral symphony. Avant-garde poet and musician Ron Geesin apparently arranged the sprawling piece, although strangely he doesn't get any credits for it. Performed live, the Atom Heart Mother Suite is like an extended blues jam. On the album, the choral symphonic framework provides for a somewhat surrealistic composition with boring results and pompous musical ambitions. On side two, we are treated to a series of rather one-dimensional songs, like the dull If and The Beatlesque Summer Of '68. David Gilmour's soaring guitar lines on Fat Old Sun tug the heartstrings, but fail to keep the flat song alive. Alan's Psychedelic Breakfast, the album's conclusion, is plain silly. Who on earth wants to hear the recorded sounds of a Floydian breakfast? Are we missing the point? Is this a subtle display of Cantabrigian humour or were they just simply bored out of their minds? At least they could have given us a grand finale with the dynamics of Astronomy Domine or Set The Controls For The Heart Of The Sun. There is nothing wrong with the odd joke or occasional experiment, but venturing in many bizarre directions, Atom Heart Mother comes to too many dead ends, leaving the listener in utter confusion.

Matt Hallander, Rock Parade

21
FEARLESS

Abbey Road, St. John's Wood, London, May 27, 1971

"So, you didn't like Atom Heart Mother?" Nick Mason asked, faking his worst, most evil scowl.

"Guilty as charged, your honour."

"Careful, defendant, you're taking the piss out of our first ever number one album," Nick laughed. The drummer's standalone moustache had gone, a full beard now growing in its stead.

"Don't listen to him, Matt. I'm with you on this," Roger Waters said. "It's an awful and embarrassing record."

"It's our weirdest shit so far, that's for sure," David Gilmour put in.

Rick Wright said nothing, but he didn't look upset.

The band had gathered in one of the studio's control rooms to kick off a new day of recording. I was there as a lucky guest, invited along to write the next episode in my Pink Floyd story.

"You can't call it 'shit'. That's unfair," Mason retorted, shooting David a look. "It was a good idea, just not very well executed."

Nick turned back to me. "We had a problem with the backing tracks. We should've recorded the backing tracks and the click track and then added the rhythm track afterwards. But Roger and I were uneasy about playing to a click track. We wanted to get our stuff laid down first. So the rhythm track was a little erratic, and that meant the orchestra struggled a bit with the beat. I guess that was our fault. The sound quality isn't as good as it should be for an orchestra either. The choir part Ron wrote for Funky Dung works best."

"Funky Dung..." Gilmour sighed.

"Which genius decided we should call some of our weirdest shit Funky Dung?" Roger asked with a sarcastic grin on his face.

Nobody felt the need to reply.

"I have no idea why we fouled it up. I think we weren't quite ready for it," Roger continued.

"There are just too many edits on it," Richard Wright said, joining the conversation. "It doesn't flow well. But I enjoy playing it live."

"Oh man, I'll never forget the look on Wood's face when we showed him the cover." Roger laughed.

David leaned over and explained: "Wood is the managing director of EMI's Record Division."

"'Ah, Friesians'. I swear that was his first reaction," Nick added with a twinkle in his eyes. "And then he yelled at Storm: 'Are you mad? Do you want to destroy this record company?' Poor Storm. But please don't tell anyone we told you this, okay Matt?"

I just smiled.

"They probably weren't in a good mood, anyway," added one of the engineers who'd introduced himself earlier as Peter Brown. "A few weeks before EMI had been shown the cover art, we had one of their guys come over to the studio wanting to hear the album. What he didn't know was Roger and Ron had hidden a turntable under the desk and they played an old 78 rpm disc through the studio speakers. The

A&R guy looked totally baffled and walked out. Priceless!"

Everyone around me nodded and laughed.

It wasn't a surprise Pink Floyd didn't particularly like their last album. I didn't like it either, as I'd made clear in Rock Parade. The band had read the review and found it "somewhat annoying," but thought that I maybe had a point. I later learned from my contacts at the record company, that they'd invited me to the studio because they'd enjoyed the interview at Charlton Park. I must admit to feeling enormously proud of myself for a few days after hearing that. Now that they were working on a new project, the band probably felt they had something to prove: that they could do better than Atom Heart Mother. When the official invite came in, my editor thought that I should be the one to pick the Pink Floyd trail up again. As it also meant I'd get the chance to see the place where The Beatles recorded Sgt. Pepper. How could I refuse?

After the band left the control room to work on its set-up in the studio below, Peter pulled a tape from a box and said: "Hope you're sitting comfortably. The track I'm going to play you is almost 24 minutes long. It's not finished yet, mind you."

I looked at the label on the empty box, 'Nothings', it said.

"What's it called?" I asked.

"They're not sure yet," Peter replied. "When they play it live, they refer to it as 'The Return of the Son of Nothing', but I'm sure there will be some tweaking of song titles before they release the album. OK, here we go."

The first thing I heard was a 'ping', like the signal destroyer vessels use when searching for submarines; a sound straight out of a wartime movie. Then another one, followed by more pings. Then some organ sounds and the first few subtle notes of a guitar. A minute later, the sounds melted into an intriguing intro, followed by bass, drums and melody. I felt goosebumps puff up the hairs on my skin. By the time David started to sing, I knew Pink Floyd had not only found their new direction, they'd also opened the door to a world filled with unexplored possibilities. I listened in awe. It was indeed a long piece, but completely coherent and full of musical suspense. Bluesy Hammond licks, funky bass rhythms, rigorous drumbeats, haunting and howling guitar riffs. It somehow all made sense. Pink Floyd had struck gold. No doubt about it. This was exactly the sort of music I'd been waiting for all my life.

"What do you think?" Peter asked when he returned to the control room.

"I... I don't know what to say. I'm speechless. It's the best thing I've ever heard. Honestly!"

"Glad you like it. Go tell the boys, they're in Studio 3. I'm sure they are ready for some compliments."

Filled with excitement, I ran down the stairs.

"Hey guys," I called out, pushing open the doors to the recording room, "you may call them nothings, but I find them nothing less than brilliant! I am sure this is going to be your best album ever!"

The room was a jumble of wires with speakers and headphones strewn literally everywhere. Nick, who'd just finished attaching a cymbal to its stand, was the first to reply.

"It seems we're finally doing something good around here."

Roger, his hands full of cables, laughed and said: "It's about fuckin' time!"

Rick, who was fiddling about with an organ, turned and gave me a wide grin. David looked over from behind a stack of amps and said: "Thanks, Matt. Glad you like it."

Then they all went back to working on the gear. I walked

over to Rick.

"How on earth did you come up with that ping sound?"

"It wasn't complicated," he explained. "I just hit a single note on the piano and played it through a Leslie speaker."

"It sounds like a submarine hunter."

"Yeah, I know. We actually recorded it for a demo, but I think we're going to use it on the record."

"It works like a dream and it gives the song a little extra, an edge."

"Thanks, we're quite happy with it ourselves. We're all into experimenting with sounds, you know. See that yellow device in front of the guitar amps?"

I nodded.

"It's a Binson Echorec, an echo unit made in Italy. It produces a unique sound. We've been using it for years now. Do you remember hearing a violin on the Nothings track?"

I nodded, again.

"That's David playing through the Binson. He's using it for another song we're working on today."

Oddly enough, David was tuning a bass, not a guitar. Each note he played resonated at least four or five times.

"Have we got the new strings, yet?" I heard him ask through a microphone.

"Nope," a voice coming out of an intercom speaker replied.

"What the hell?"

"Sorry, David, I'll let you know when he's back."

"OK, we'll start with this set first, then. Ready, Rog?"

Roger and David started to play their basses in unison. They were checking on each other, playing back and forth, switching between playing for only a couple of seconds to stretches of a minute or more. Together they produced dark, thumping, pounding sounds. They tried it over and over, searching for the right groove and feel. Nick, headphones on head, was sitting behind his kit, ready and waiting for his cue. Rick, meanwhile, was trying out some chords to fit with the two basses. I couldn't tell if they were rehearsing or recording, but it was good to see them working together like that. As a team. Concentrated and dedicated. Not smiling much, but obviously enjoying what they were doing. And it sounded great.

I felt hugely privileged to be in the room with them. Nobody objected or seemed to be bothered by my presence, but being a bystander somehow didn't feel quite right. Deciding to leave them to it, I left Studio 3 as quietly as I could and headed for the recreational area.

▪ ▪ ▪

I got myself a coffee, picked up a copy of The Times and plonked myself down onto a comfy leather couch. I read the international news and the sports pages, and scanned the entertainment section for any music-related news. After roughly an hour, I noticed two guys down the hallway speaking in rather agitated tones. It was clear some row was going on.

"Man, we've been waiting for hours. You've ruined the recording session."

"Oh, come on, it's just a set of strings."

"But we bloody well needed them. What took you so long, anyway?"

"What do you mean?"

"You left the studio three hours ago. Can't be that hard to find the music shop."

"Chill out, dude, I'm here with the strings, aren't I?"

"Just way too late. Somebody told me you were visiting your girlfriend."

"My girlfriend?"

"Yeah, man, you know, the one that runs the boutique."

"What's the big deal? I got what you wanted. What makes you think I was visiting my friend?"

"Honestly, man, it's quite obvious, isn't it?"

"What?"

"Those new pants you're wearing. Pretty smart, aren't they? I am sure you left in an old and dirty pair of jeans."

"Fuck you, man! I don't have to listen to this shit!"

"Just hand me the strings and get out of here."

I chuckled, picked up another newspaper from the table and continued reading. Just as I was about to leave the studio, tired of waiting and knowing I could come back tomorrow, Roger, David and Nick showed up.

"Done for the day?" I asked.

"I wish," Nick replied.

"Lunch break," Roger said. "A long overdue lunch break, I might add."

"Seen the sandwiches, Matt?"

"Sorry, I ate them all."

"You'd better not have if you want to leave this place alive," Roger joked. "I'll check the kitchen."

A few minutes later, Roger arrived with a plate full of assorted sandwiches and a big bowl of crisps. They attacked the food as if they were starving. Maybe they were.

"I really like this place," I said, trying to keep up the conversation. "From the outside, this building looks like the offices of some big international law firm. Standing in the parking lot out front, you'd never guess that you're looking at the most famous recording studio in the world."

"You mean famous because we're recording in it, Matt?"

"You wish. There's this other band that recorded here, you know. What was their name, again? The Crickets, or something? Odd bunch of guys from Liverpool."

"They were making Pepper when we were recording Piper," Roger said. "McCartney used to come into our studio. I don't know why, but he's a bit of a fan. He wanted to see what we were doing. 'Ello! Alright?' I don't remember whether George Martin was here too, but Geoff Emerick was. He's a brilliant engineer. John Lennon for sure was in here. Not that he'd ever acknowledge our presence though, let alone speak to us. You should check out the space between the two sets of soundproof doors that open onto the main entrance of Studio 2. The Mellotron is in there."

"The Mellotron?" I asked.

"Strawberry Fields, you dimwit!" Roger replied, rolling his eyes.

"They were busy recording Lovely Rita," Nick recalled. "The music sounded wonderful and they were incredibly professional. We sat humbly at the back of the control room while they worked on the mix. After a bit, it felt kind of embarrassing and we were ushered out again."

"Sounds just like me in Studio 3 today," I deadpanned.

"They're great at making singles," I teased.

Roger took the bait: "You have to work to your strength, Matt. It's a good thing we can't write singles. Otherwise we wouldn't have done some of the things we do. But we're always exploring new territories."

"We like to push boundaries back a little," David Gilmour said, joining the conversation: "We're always looking for new ways to move forward, experimenting, seeing what might work on a track. But we want to keep the melody in there, too. We really love to jam away in these studio rooms."

"So, who pens the lyrics?" I asked.

"Roger usually has a thing or two to say," Richard interjected, appearing out of nowhere and going straight for the remaining stack of sandwiches.

"You like to work with tape loops and sound effects," I stated.

Nick nodded. "Yes, but working on those loops can be a bit of a nuisance because we have to do all the timing with hand signs and stopwatches."

"The first take of a song is usually the best one, anyway. You start repeating yourself after that." David said.

No one disagreed. It was remarkable to have all band members engaged in conversation. They were usually far less forthcoming. Except for Nick, the other three could happily sit there and say nothing, just minding their own business and observing what was going on. Unlike your typical extravagant pop stars, these musicians were reserved, introverted Englishmen who probably still can't believe they are trying to make a living out of playing instruments and writing songs.

"Has studying architecture benefitted the way you construct new music?" I asked, switching to full reporter mode.

"More than you'd think," Nick replied enthusiastically, obviously pleased by the question.

"It helps us to translate strange ideas into reality," he added. "In knowing which of our ideas will never work, and to see the bigger picture; to get a feel of the end result while we're still working out the details."

"I find it interesting that although you were born and raised in a university community like Cambridge, and some of you studied Architecture, your backgrounds are all middle class. No offence at all."

"None taken. We're no different from most people," Nick explained. "In the 1950s, rock 'n' roll was essentially working class. It was the happy entertainment music most people listened to. That changed completely in the sixties when further education became affordable and middle class kids like us got to go to art school. The generation that emerged from that had different, experimental ideas. We're typically middle class in the way we organise things around here."

"In what way?" I asked, sensing this lunchtime conversation might be a rare opportunity to get into some more personal details. The others looked at Nick with apprehension.

"Em," he hesitated, "Maybe it's the way we communicate. We're all pretty articulate, but there are certain things we never discuss. Perhaps that's just a British thing."

The band was listening, curious to hear what Nick had to say. But it was David who continued.

"We are very English. I wouldn't want to live anywhere other than England. Even our early stuff with Syd is quintessentially English. Just like the Kinks, or The Who. I like to believe that everything we do has an English accent. Do you think we succeed, Matt?"

"Yes, I think you do. Production-wise, for sure. And the lyrics. I can't think of any American artist wanting to sing about a Corporal Clegg and his wooden leg!"

Roger laughed.

"That's exactly my point," he said. I love writing lyrics. I find it so frustrating some fans think all our songs are about outer space. It's because of Interstellar Overdrive, you know. And Astronomy Domine. They're both Syd's. His lyrics are far more to do with his attachment to English literature. For me, it is all about personal experience and has nothing to do with the firmament."

"And you, David," I asked, "do you like writing lyrics, as well?"

"Dave is a great singer," Roger sneered before David could say anything. He looked like he'd just scored a point.

Ignoring him, David answered: "It isn't my strongest point. I rather let my guitar do the talking." And after a brief pause for thought, added: "I love singing, though. I try to spend as much time working on improving my voice as I do on practicing guitar."

"I'm no Bob Dylan or Neil Young, either," Roger admitted. "But I enjoy writing, thinking, producing. And I enjoy playing in this band. The bread is good, but the real reward is the work."

With that, the lunchtime conversation was over. Richard had already gone, probably back to Studio 3, and Nick was chitchatting with one of the girls who worked in the canteen. Roger stood up to pour himself another cup of coffee while David and I continued talking about the weeks to follow. He mentioned the band was going to be moving around studios to finish recording their new album, including George Martin's. He also talked about their visit to the US earlier that year, saying they'd really enjoyed it and were already planning to go back. I told David just how interested I'd be in doing a road story, and what a perfect setting touring America would be for my next Pink Floyd feature. I could barely contain my excitement when he said Pink Floyd could do with the extra publicity and that I was more than welcome to contact Steve O'Rourke about it.

David excused himself and left me feeling over the moon. My journey with Pink Floyd had not yet come to an end. Thanks to a recently recorded set of 'nothings' I could look forward to some exciting times ahead. Go figure!

23
CHILDHOOD'S END

USA & Canada tour, March 1973

"Yesterday, one of our backing singers disappeared. And guess what? She was arrested with her boyfriend for holding up a grocery shop!"

"No way!"

"I'm not making this up. I've seen some weird things on the road, but this is a first."

I was half sitting, half lying on the back bench of the tour bus. My legs were still hurting from last night's gig at Toronto's Maple Leaf Gardens, my feet up were on the empty seat in front of me. I'd send my suggestion following the Floyd from Toronto to New York to the Rock Parade editor, and to my surprise he'd agreed. I'd arrived at the impressive Canadian venue just in time for the soundcheck, and road manager Peter Watts had offered me to let me ride with them on the crew bus to Montreal, and possibly even on to Boston the next day. I couldn't believe my luck. Not only did it spare me a couple of lonely train rides, but it also meant I could observe the Pink Floyd live circus from up close.

A lot had changed since I'd seen the guys in the Abbey Road Studios. Meddle had turned out to be a commercial and creative success. The release was followed by more touring in bigger venues, the filming of a performance in an ancient Roman amphitheatre in Pompeii, Italy, the release of Obscured By Clouds and a performance with a French ballet. Topping all that, the band had also found time to record their brand-new LP Dark Side Of The Moon. The album had its official US premiere only two days ago, so the whole Floyd entourage was in a state of excitement. And so was I. Last night in Toronto, the band played the Dark Side Of The Moon in its entirely. To say it had impressed me would be a huge understatement. I'd witnessed an overpowering quadraphonic adventure with an intriguing set of songs and a nothing less than spectacular light show.

So band and crew had every reason to be in a good mood, and the travelling entourage seemed perfectly fine at having an extra passenger on board. Arriving in Toronto, one of the first people I bumped into was Abbey Road's tall studio engineer, Alan Parsons. Alan had since been promoted to 'front of the house sound engineer' as they now officially called it. I also met Chris, the back-line tech, Graeme, who did lighting, a Polish guy called Mick who operated the tapes and the quad sound, and saxophone player Dick Parry, who'd played some remarkable solos during last night's Dark Side set. Besides these fine fellows, Pink Floyd had hired four guys to drive the two massive forty-foot trailer trucks from city to city.

Sitting next to me on the back bench of the bus was Peter Watts. As I found out, Peter used to work for The Pretty Things crew but had joined the Floyd a couple of months before David Gilmour. Peter was a great talking companion, and we were soon swapping road stories.

"Have you heard the new Alice Cooper album?" I asked.

"No, not yet. Is it any good?"

"I like it. Some catchy songs and a neat production by Bob

Ezrin."

"There's this story," I went on, "that Alice bit off a chicken's head and drunk its blood on stage."

"I know that story! It's not true, though," Peter asserted. "From what I was told, Alice and his band had been travelling with two chickens they called Larry and Pecker. They treated those chickens like pets, but it seems they were victims of a stage stunt that went horribly wrong. Alice, apparently assuming that because chickens have wings they can fly, picked one up and threw it out over the audience, fully expecting it to flap away. Instead, the chicken flopped into the crowd and some people ripped the poor bird to pieces. The following day, the incident made headlines, and some newspapers reported Cooper had bitten off the chicken's head and drunk its blood on stage. Alice denied the rumour, of course, and in an attempt to get himself off the hook with the animal protection organisations, instead claimed some punters had thrown the chicken onstage."

"Only in rock 'n' roll," I laughed.

"But it gets even better," Peter continued.

"The next day, Alice got a phone call from Frank Zappa, who ran the band's label. 'Did you kill the chicken onstage?' Frank asked. 'No,' Alice replied. 'Well, don't tell anybody.' Frank advised. 'Everybody loves it. You are the most notorious character of all time now.'"

"That's hilarious! Maybe I should talk to Roger and ask him to bring some real pigs along on tour."

"Did you know the Alice Cooper band are big fans of Pink Floyd? Glen Buxton once told me he could listen to Syd Barrett's guitar for hours at a time."

We continued swapping stories for a while, then Peter got up and left me to my own devices for the rest of the trip. I didn't mind as I was longing for a few hours much-needed rest. With the back seats all to myself, I let the soothing rhythm of the bus send me to sleep.

▪ ▪ ▪

As soon as we arrived in Montreal, everybody swung into action. It was as if they each had a scripted role to play. Watching the busy crew from the sidelines, my lack of activity soon felt out of place and I asked one guy if he could do with an extra pair of hands. Before I knew it, I was humping flight cases full of merchandise towards the front entrance of the venue.

The thumbs up I got from Peter spurred me on until there was nothing left for me to do, so I hung around admiring the roadies for the pace and precision with which they were building up the stage. Lights first, instruments next, cables last. It was a well-trained crew, like an army of soldiers, except nobody was shouting or giving orders. Everybody knew exactly what to do, except maybe for the local crew. They just did what they were told.

It only took a couple of hours from start to finish, which seemed like a massive achievement considering the amount of stuff and people involved. To kill some time, I went to explore the floors of this impressive ice rink. Quite a step up from the old Amsterdam Paradiso, I thought. Soaking in the empty grandeur of the place, I took some pictures with the cheap Nikon I'd bought second hand from the local camera shop just days before we'd left. With my pass firmly stuck on my coat I could go wherever I liked. It felt rather good, as if my status as trusted member of this travelling gang had been given the seal of approval.

When everything was set up and ready, the band, as if on cue, walked on stage and started to tune their instruments and test the mics. There didn't seem to be much order to the proceedings; the constant back and forth between the house and monitor mixers was all mumbo jumbo to me. But I knew I was watching a dyed-in-the-wool operation, with Roger definitely at the helm. So now I know who gives the orders, I thought, making a mental note to explore that angle further for my feature article: Who exactly calls the shots in Pink Floyd?

After about 15 minutes, the band played the first section of a song. There were a couple of interruptions and some sort of discussions going on, but then they played fragments from some other songs and one or two numbers from their new LP. It may only have been a soundcheck, but I was pretty stunned by the opulence of their sound. One by one, the band members left the stage, only Richard remained behind, checking his keyboards with a sound tech by his side.

With the soundcheck done, most of the crew wandered off to one of the larger backstage rooms to have dinner. I followed. Dinner turned out to be a school meal type buffet and didn't look all that inviting, but when Peter Watts nodded, as if to say: 'go ahead, you're a part of the crew now, grab a bite,' I had no option but to join the queue. Pasta or rice. Typical road food. I went for the rice, topped it with a yellowish curry sauce, and added greens on the side. Plate in hand, I grabbed a can of Coca Cola and sat down at one of the long tables. The food tasted bloody awful. After a couple of spoonsful of rice minus the curry, I'd had enough and pushed my plate away. I took my notebook out of the inside pocket of my jacket and scribbled a few observations: 'Calling the shots...'

I had little to write yet, but it helped to make me look busy. Not that anybody showed a blind bit of interest in me at all.

Out of the corner of my eye I saw Nick Mason saunter in, followed on his heels by David Gilmour. They exchanged a few words with the crew then David plucked a banana from the fruit bowl leaving Nick behind to crack a few jokes with Chris and Graeme.

"What happens if you play country music backwards?" I heard him ask. After a few seconds of silence, he spread both arms and delivered the punch line: "You sober up, get a job, and your wife comes back!"

I liked Nick for his cheerful smiles and uplifting presence. He was never without a good story to tell. I don't think I'd ever seen him in a foul mood, either; quite some achievement being in a band with messieurs Water and Gilmour and their erratic tempers. You never knew where you were with them, depending on how last night's performance had gone, the sound quality and how well each of them had played. Peter told me he never heard them complain about hotels or transport, but crappy acoustics, an inadequate sound guy, or one of them playing the wrong key or pace would throw them into an apoplectic rage. I found that weirdly amusing for a band that used to revel in psychedelic chaos and disorder.

I wasn't surprised Waters' mood swings were notorious. With Roger, what you see is what you get. David is more balanced. Wrapped in a thick layer of quintessentially English armour, he doesn't get mad at people and seldom raises his voice. His weapons are wit, and a swift and snappy way with words. He gets his point over perfectly well with effortlessly thrown out bon mots, puns and one liners. Independently of each other, Roger and David can be pretty mean. But if they're fighting to uphold a Pink Floyd cause, the combined fury of the two is nothing less than lethal. Just ask the poor tech hire who'd been found kipping during last night's Toronto gig. Luckily, Nick had saved his ass by joking that Pink Floyd obviously didn't play loud enough. It occurred to me that perhaps Nick Mason and his comic relief were the reason Pink Floyd had made it this far.

I still had to figure Richard Wright out. I liked him a lot, both as a musician and as a human being. He was quiet and polite. Like David, I've never seen Rick angry, but I've never seen him overcome with laughter and joy either. In fact, I suddenly realised, I had absolutely no clue what sort of person Rick really is.

Nick Mason walked over. "Hey, Matt, good to see you're still hanging around. Not fed up with us old farts, yet?"

I smiled.

"I'll take that as a 'no' then. Nice hairdo, by the way," he said, pointing at my head.

"Anything you can do, I can do better." I countered, smiling.

"We're pretty good at skipping appointments with our hairdressers..."

"I'm trying to save some money."

"Good for you, mate. I'm off to the hotel now, but don't forget to look us up after the show. Looking forward to hear what you think of the new stuff. Cheerio!"

▪ ▪ ▪

After a brilliant show in Montreal, I skipped the gig in Philadelphia, took the train to New York and re-joined the band for the last gig of my private Pink Floyd tour. I had grossly overestimated the charm of backstage life. Hanging around these empty venues had quickly become a bore. The band was busy promoting their new album and when they weren't doing the radio stations, interviews or photo shoots, they were grabbing an hour or two's sleep back at the hotel. They rarely showed up until it was time for soundcheck, and mostly went straight back as soon as it was done. That left me with nothing to do but talk with the crew, fellow journalists, fans and, if I was lucky, one of the band's wives or girlfriends. I'd met Richard's wife, Juliette, at Charlton Park briefly, but I hadn't seen her on this tour. Peter Watts had introduced me to Roger's wife, Judy, Nick's wife, Lindy, and David's Ginger in Toronto.

The backstage area of the New York Radio City Music Hall, the world's largest indoor theatre, was already buzzing with friends, relatives and hangers-on. Soundcheck had not been done yet, so I busied myself with taking photos of the stunning building. The auditorium was enormous, with layers and layers of plush red seats looking out at a huge stage framed by a series of arches that extended out like the rays of a setting sun.

Part of the appeal of touring, especially with a band busting out big time, is that you get to a bunch of different venues in as many locations. Each has its own distinctive vibe, but this one here in the Big Apple was over and above special. It was truly magnificent. For me, the greatest high of all was the atmosphere. It was amazing and literally much warmer than Montreal's ice rink. The show was a complete sell out, with the guest list alone occupying all of the first two rows, as I was told earlier by a somewhat grumpy promoter. Absolutely everybody wanted to see Pink Floyd play in New York. And the tension was rising tangibly.

Steve O'Rourke joined us backstage, acting very nervous. He was walking around talking and gesturing all over the place. He either didn't see me or ignored me completely. That wasn't a bad thing. Over the past few days, I'd learned that at times like these, out of Steve's firing line was way better than in. Fortunately, there were plenty of women around and they seemed to be soothing things a bit. With lower testosterone levels and less foul language, the place had a familiar, almost intimate feel.

David and Ginger passed me in the corridor, holding hands and smiling. David nodded a quick "Matt" to acknowledge my presence, and the pair turned into the band's designated dressing room. David tossed his leather jacket onto a chair and without closing the door, kissed Ginger on the cheek and came straight back out again. Off to join the rest of the band, I guessed.

I walked over to Ginger.

"Can I get you something? A coffee? Soda? A beer? Anything?"

"A cup of tea would be great. Thank you."

"Don't go away. I'll be back in a sec."

I walked to the crew catering area, put two teas, some milk and sugar on a tray, and went back to the dressing room. Ginger was sitting on a red sofa. I placed the tea on a small table in front of her.

"Thanks, that's real sweet of you," she said.

I followed her eyes as they glanced over at a long dressing table in front of a row of mirrors, each surrounded by bright white light bulbs. There, in front of the Hollywood-style make-up mirrors, stood a kettle, a basket full of assorted teas, various drinks in ice buckets, fruit, snacks, sandwiches, the lot. I felt foolish.

Seeing my embarrassment, Ginger laughed and said: "No worries. Come, have a seat."

I sat on a chair opposite the sofa and picked up my tea.

With long wavy blond hair and a pale angelic face, Ginger was quite lovely.

"We met a few days ago, didn't we, Matt?" she asked.

"Yes, we did. Peter introduced us in Toronto," said, surprised she remembered my name.

"But I don't think I saw you in Philadelphia."

"No, I skipped that one. How do you know I wasn't there?" I asked, puzzled.

"I was born in Philadelphia, so I invited my parents over and introduced them to everybody in the crew. Well, nearly everybody."

"Sorry to miss that. But I'm not really part of the crew," I explained.

"Oh, are you a fan?"

"I'm a journalist. Writing for a UK music magazine. But, yes, I'm a fan, too. Have been since I first saw the band play. That was in Amsterdam, back in 1968."

"I've never been to Amsterdam, but I'd love to go there."

"I hope you don't mind me asking," I said, trying to be polite while not letting the conversation end, "how did you and David meet?"

Her face lit up and she told me her and David's story.

"We met in October two years ago. The band was playing at a festival in Michigan, my hometown, along with Quicksilver and various local bands. I remember it well. They played Embryo, Fat Old Sun, Set The Controls For The Heart of Sun, and some other songs. We were all spellbound. The friends I was with knew the band's roadie, Chris Adamson, so after the gig we all went backstage. That's where David and I first met. He was wearing a black t-shirt with 'That's All Folks' written on it and came up and introduced himself. Being the shy person I am, we only exchanged a few words."

Ginger paused a few seconds and continued. "Believe it or not, my friends wanted me to invite the band and crew over for dinner the next evening, so I did, and they accepted. When they arrived at our place, I cooked dinner while David sat on the ground sifting through our albums and being our DJ for the evening. The band wanted to see Quicksilver, so we agreed we'd all meet at the concert the next day, and go on afterwards to a Halloween roller skating party in Detroit. When we got to the festival, Steve O'Rourke suggested I sit next to David, so we watched the Quicksilver gig together. What I didn't know was that someone had given him some Mescaline that night. So there I was, sitting next to the man of my dreams, holding hands, while David was tripping."

She stopped.

"I don't want you to write about this, Matt. I can trust you, can't I?"

"Of course you can. Scouts honour!"

"Thank you, I'd rather keep our private lives out of the press, if you know what I mean."

I nodded.

"After the concert," Ginger continued, "we all went back to my house and David and I had our first kiss. Then we jumped back in the car and drove off to Detroit for the party. I remember, on the way, Orson Welles' War Of The Worlds was being broadcast on the radio. The band had never heard it, and by the time we reached Detroit, some of them were tripping out because they thought the Martians had landed."

"Very romantic! How did the skating go?"

"David couldn't skate very well, but he said I was a 'dream on wheels'. Such a sweetheart. When it was time for the band to leave, David slipped me his parents' phone number and asked me to call him. I was in another relationship at the time. David knew about it, but it was all very confusing and I had to make a choice. I followed my heart and a few days later, when the band was playing in New Jersey, we met up again in New York."

It turned out that David's parents, Doug, a geneticist, and

Sylvia, a film editor, lived in New York and Ginger had met them at the Carnegie Hall. Ginger moved to the UK not long after and was now living with David in his 16th century house in rural Oxfordshire. The house had its own stables and a few barns and she kept a duck, two cats and a horse called Vim. It all sounded pretty idyllic. The couple were good friends with Steve Marriott of Humble Pie and his wife Jenny, who lived close by. They would meet up most weeks when the Floyd wasn't touring. We all knew Steve's dog Seamus, of course, the collie that did the outstanding howling job on Meddle.

After a while, the band returned from the soundcheck and getting up to leave them to themselves, I thanked Ginger for the great stories. David's eyes flicked to mine, an eyebrow raised in a silent question. I moved the tip of my forefinger and thumb in one quick horizontal movement across my lips. Zipped. We all laughed.

▪ ▪ ▪

I wandered around, looking for a bite to eat and the best spot for tonight's show. With my pass, I could probably even watch it from the side of the stage, like I'd seen some of the band's VIPs do at earlier gigs. But standing in the wings didn't do it for me. Pink Floyd's audio-visual spectacle had to be experienced in front of the stage. A better view and way better sound.

After the lights dimmed, clouds of steam shot up from vents in the stage. The band rose into view on one of the elevators and inched forward out of the mist. An immense sphere, mounted on futuristic light towers, cast mirror dots and needle-like red lasers throughout the hall. The effect was hypnotic, and the crowd roared out their approval. Obscured By Clouds and David's haunting guitar licks rolled majestically from the quad system. With twenty speakers on all levels of the hall, we were treated to the eerie effect of being surrounded by the musical magic.

The intro segued into the long, bluesy riffs of When You're In. I heard someone in the audience say "man, it feels like I'm on trip." That summed it up nicely, and I couldn't have wished for a better opening. Next up were Set The Controls For The Heart Of The Sun, Echoes, and a bristling tense version of Careful With That Axe, Eugene. The second half was a fabulous rendition of the entire The Dark Side Of The Moon. Pink Floyd's light and sound crew never seemed to miss a cue, and their arsenal of very cool experimental sounds had enhanced the surround sound experience of the show. This was no gimmickry. The power and dynamics completely blew me away.

Still high on adrenaline, I arrived back in the backstage area. The spacious rooms and hallways were filled with people talking, laughing and shouting. They were an odd mix. I recognised some relatives and a few record company executives, but there were also lots of fans and people I hadn't seen before. These areas can be disturbingly quiet after a show to the point where you wonder if you are at the right venue. Tonight was completely the opposite. I'd never seen a backstage area so crowded.

There were snacks and every kind of drink imaginable scattered around, and I got the feeling this was going to be one hell of an afterparty. I was flying back home first thing in the morning and going easy on the booze. I was so incredibly proud of tonight's momentous event and felt an immense sense of gratitude towards the great people I'd come to know over the last few days. Saying 'hi' to any faces I thought I may know, I gently navigated my way through the hustle and bustle. The band had a lot more important people than me they needed to attend to and they were all already deep in conversation. Most of the crew was busy too, packing up and loading in. Stone cold sober as I was, I began to feel a bit alienated from the festivities.

Deciding to take myself back to the hotel, I put on my green army coat and headed for the exit. On my way, I passed one of the few quiet dressing rooms and saw Rick Wright sitting there, alone. He was sprawled over a chair, legs stretched out and arms hanging loosely over the sides. I put my head around the door.

"Hi Richard! How's it going?"

"Good, thanks Matt. Just taking a breather. Come on in. Want a beer?"

I grabbed a bottle of Bud from the fridge and dropped onto the chair next to him.

"Pizza?" he asked, pointing at the slices in the open box.

"Sure, thanks." I picked the smallest slice, took a bite. "Tonight's show was massive. The sound was phenomenal and the new songs are brilliant. It was probably the best show I've seen so far."

"It was alright," Richard replied, his voice a bit subdued. "I had some minor technical issues, nothing important."

"You sound disappointed."

"Yeah. I had a kind of... um..." Richard searched for the word, "... fallout with Roger tonight. I got angry because he was playing out of tune. I hate things being out of tune. We were in D and he was still banging away in E because he couldn't hear it. I had to tune his bass onstage, you know. He didn't like it."

I tried to soften things a little.

"You and Roger are solar opposites, aren't you?"

"We can be snappy with each other sometimes, for sure," Richard admitted.

"Why's that?"

"I guess it goes all the way back to the Polytechnic days. The two of us didn't really get on even then. Being the person he is, Roger would try, well… to rile you, if you like, get you to crack. There's been some sort of personal strife thing going on between us ever since. We don't always see eye to eye politically, either. I'm not right-wing or anything, but when we finally earned some money, I bought a house in the country. Rog couldn't believe it. He told me he thought it was disgusting and accused me of selling out. Now he's bought his own, much bigger country house. He claims it was his wife that wanted it, that it's not for himself. But for me it's hypocritical. And it makes me angry."

"I'm sorry to hear. The band always sounds really tight on stage, though."

"We may not be the best of mates," Richard continued, "and as individuals we are all very different, but that doesn't affect the way we play. Work-wise we're pretty much of one mind, trying to reach our common destination. Which, I guess, bottom line, is to make some money."

"Do you and David get along?" I asked.

"We're pals, sure. But David's a hard person to get to know. I probably am, too. We're not mates like we'll sit in a pub and have a gas together. We're not that close. Being with each other 24 hours a day means you sometimes get on each other's nerves. But we're always all very professional on stage."

"You've come a long way from that first gig I saw in Amsterdam. You've really progressed as a band. The songs are more lucid and direct, and much easier to listen to. There has to be some special musical chemistry going on between the four of you."

"I'd like to think so. It all dates back to when we first formed the band and Syd was doing the writing. We're much better musicians now, but if we hadn't gone through our experimental phase, we wouldn't be here today."

I took another bite from the now cold slice of pizza.

"So, what are you good at, Matt?" Richard suddenly asked.

I almost choked. What am I good at? I didn't see that coming. It took a good few seconds of serious pizza chomping before I'd calmed myself enough to come up with an answer. My mind was a blank.

"I don't know," I answered sheepishly.

"Do you want to become a professional writer? A journalist?"

"I really don't know." I heard myself mumbling again.

"There must be at least something you like doing?" he persevered, looking at me questioningly.

"Well, I know I enjoy writing, but I'm not sure if I'm any good at it. I like travelling and photography, too. And music. But I haven't figured out where I want to go with it all yet. I'd like to have a proper job, make money, find a nice place to live. That's the simple life version of what I want, I guess. But there's also a voice telling me I ought to write a book. And learn to play an instrument. I just don't know."

"You need to find out what your talents are, Matt. Follow your heart, do what feels right."

"I know. And I want to. But I've only just finished school. I will have to work out a plan of some sort. Maybe I'll stick to writing. Not sure if I can make a living out of writing, though."

"We weren't sure about making a living out of playing music, either," Richard said, trying to reassure me.

"That's easy for you to say. You know what you're good at. I feel I suck at everything I do."

"Don't be so hard on yourself. You're young and there will be plenty of opportunities coming your way. Maybe you should become Roger's real estate broker."

"Or his bass tuning tech," I said.

We both laughed.

Richard got up saying it was time he showed his face at the party, and off he went.

I was left standing alone in an empty dressing room. Time to go home. As I hit the cold New York streets, I couldn't help thinking about the bright future that lay ahead for Pink Floyd. My future? I had absolutely no clue.

24
GREEN IS THE COLOUR

Sunningdale Golf Club, May 18, 1974

"FORE!"

The guy who'd introduced himself earlier as Nick Sedgwick yelled at the top of his lungs. I didn't know what was scarier: Sedgwick's sudden outburst or Roger's ball flying straight towards the players on the adjacent 18th fairway. Fortunately, they ducked just in time, cradling their heads in their arms. His ball had missed one golfer by a mere two yards. Roger raised his hand high to convey his apology. We were off to a good start.

While Nick teed up, Roger handed me his driver. Putting on my most serious face, took it, replaced the head cover and put it back in the bag.

"I should have made you sign a non-disclosure, Matt," Roger said. "But be warned, I will deny every word you write about this day."

"Don't worry, Jack Nicklaus. Your mishits are safe with me."

"Gentlemen, please, I'm trying to concentrate here," Nick said, and drove his ball straight as an arrow onto the fairway of hole 1.

I'd called Roger a few days ago to tell him I was going to

be in his area for a day and ask if it would be convenient for me to drop round to say 'hi'. I knew Pink Floyd wouldn't be touring for another month, so I thought it at least worth the try. He'd apologised initially, saying he was busy and that he had a little golf match planned with an old friend from his Cambridge days. The friend was called Nick, he told me, and used to book the band for student union gigs. He was a writer, too, he'd added. Then, quite out of the blue, Roger asked if I was any good at golf. When I told him I'd never played but liked to watch it on TV, he'd said: "Come on over. You can be my caddie. We'll have some fun and a couple of beers when we're done."

So here I was, carrying Roger's golf clubs round Sunningdale Golf Club. It was a fancy place. Immaculately landscaped, gated entrance, expensive cars in the parking lot, a very traditional-looking clubhouse and the mightiest oak tree I have ever seen. Members only, I presumed. I met Roger and Nick at the driving range 30 minutes before tee time, scheduled at 12:47.

I had no problems not being involved in their match and, luckily, Roger's golf bag wasn't too heavy on the shoulders. I enjoyed being away from the city. Apparently, Sunningdale was originally laid out on barren, open land, but there were trees everywhere now. Even to a complete rookie, the course looked challenging, with loads of heather, bunkers, and elevated greens with grassy gullies around the back and sides.

We were playing the New Course. 'New' because it opened in 1923. As I walked to where Roger's first ball had landed, comfortably in bounds on the adjacent fairway, I thought how nice it was to be outdoors in the fresh air, surrounded by beautiful scenery. All the same, I couldn't quite rid myself of a vague sense of discomfort. I'd always considered Roger to be a smart-mouthed fighting spirit on the left side of the political spectrum. Yet here we were, at a club known for its wealthy, conservative clientele. Had the guy whose band recently had us singing "new car, caviar, four-star daydream, think I'll buy me a football team" really invested his money in a golf club membership? Golf and rock 'n' roll? What the heck? I determined to find out why he'd sold his soul to the people I thought he detested. Only not here and now. I had to find the right moment.

Roger made sure he wasn't hindering anyone at the 18th and asked for his 5 iron. He then hit a great shot over some small trees, landing his ball just a yard or two past the narrow first green.

"On second thoughts, you better make a note of that!" he laughed.

"Let's see how you handle the pressure on the second tee, Arnold Palmer," I replied.

"Let's see if you're still hired as my caddie on that second tee," Roger joked back, adding "here, put my 4 iron back in the bag. You know, next to the 5 iron I asked for."

"Ouch, point taken. Won't happen again, boss."

A good start indeed.

Both men were dressed in jeans and polo shirts with trainers instead of spiked golf shoes on their feet. They were actually playing well. It came as no surprise that Roger was the more competitive of the two. What he lacked in technique, he made up for with sheer bloody-minded determination. He was out to win at all costs and at every aspect of the game, whether it was driving distance, closest-to-the-hole or putting. Nick didn't seem to mind. He and Roger had played golf before, and verbally he was easily his buddy's equal. They were both in high spirits and talked a lot between holes. All matters Pink Floyd, though, were carefully avoided. By now, Roger had a million-selling record topping the album charts, had just finished a series of long and gruelling recording sessions for yet another new LP, and was about to back on the road. The last thing he wanted, or so I figured, was to talk about work on the golf course. Instead, they touched on everything from the recent tornado outbreak in the US and the car bomb massacre in Ireland that killed 33 people to ABBA winning the Eurovision Song Contest with a song called Waterloo. All three events had shocked us, albeit with varying degrees of gravity.

Halfway through the 9th hole, we were startled when a red fox darted across the green in front of us. The sight of the shy little creature changed our conversation to matters of wildlife, hunting and fishing.

"When I was a child," Roger recalled, replacing a lump of grass into his divot, "I remember seeing a fox hunt thundering over the farmland and thinking what a spectacular sight it was. I was especially struck by the foot followers, with their Thermos flasks, ruddy complexion and excited enthusiasm. I think all rational people agree that foxes need to be controlled, so why not by hunting?"

"What's wrong with drag hunting?" Nick asked.

"That's not hunting. There's no spontaneity. People enjoy fox hunting because it is hunting. There is a quarry, that's the point. Man is a hunter. To legislate against his instinct is a folly. Most of the time I ignore the papers, but a ban on hunting? I can't let that roll off my back."

Roger was just getting started.

"The farmers and sportsmen do a pretty good job of husbanding the wild and farmed animal population. The hunting community has provided a bulwark against forces that want to bulldoze the countryside and cover it in fertiliser."

"Or turn it into a golf course," I noted.

Roger pretended not to hear me.

"I condemn the way some farmers transport livestock, and I support any legislation to bring these practices to an end. But animal husbandry in Britain is generally rather good. Without sound farming, our land could easily turn into a dust bowl. It is the huntsmen and the country people who prevent this from happening. We need these communities to remain intact if our kids are to have any countryside to enjoy at all. Now hand me my pitching wedge, please."

"As a child I used to go fishing in the Cam at Grantchester," Nick said after they'd both holed their next shots.

"Yeah, me too, man. With a bamboo pole and a bent pin. I did a lot of coarse fishing. Fighting your way down through the reeds to find a suitable spot... I always loved it. There's something about the mud between your toes."

And so the talk continued, the topic switching constantly between golf and whatever else that came to mind. Then, at the 17th hole, a par three of 170 yards with a green that falls steeply to the left and guarded with bunkers on the right, Roger suddenly said: "Here, young master Matt, it's about time you had a go."

"You're sure?" I replied. "I've never hit a golf ball before..."

"Go on, show us what you're made of."

"Nick?"

"Yeah, show us, man. Give it a good whack!"

Roger handed me a 3 wood, I teed up a ball, and took a stance like I'd seen all the pros do. After three practice swings and a lot of teasing from Roger and Nick, I took a little step forward and addressed the ball.

"Ten quid if you hit the green," I heard Nick say.

"A hundred if you hit it within five feet of the pin," Roger added.

I took a deep breath, made a real slow backswing, and let it go. The ball went a long way, but to the left. Way to the left.

"Wow!"

"I think you've just killed your first fox, Matt."

"Screw that, I'm taking a mulligan. Are the bets still on?"

"You pay us if you lose another ball," Roger replied.

"OK, stand back and watch," I bluffed.

Miraculously, the second hit was straight, landing about twenty feet short of the green.

Both Nick and Roger clapped their hands.

"Fearless!" I cried, quite overjoyed.

...

Back at the clubhouse terrace - they wouldn't let us wear jeans and trainers inside - we enjoyed a couple of well-deserved pints.

"I really enjoyed my first round of golf, even if I was just carrying the bag. But, and I mean no offence, I'm a little surprised you've applied to be a member here."

Finally, I'd summoned the courage to ask what had been on my mind the whole day.

Luckily, Roger Waters wasn't offended.

"When you've suddenly got a few quid," he explained, "you've got to decide whether to invest it or put it in the bank. You have to decide if you want to become a capitalist or not."

"And?"

"It's tempting to spend it on the things you like. Golfing at one of England's finest courses, to name one. I am trying to fight it. The sports car bit and all. It's all very tricky and hard, and we've had enormous arguments in the band about it.

Especially because I claim to have vaguely socialist principles."

"I remember the E-type Jaguar," Nick said.

"Yeah, but I never felt happy in it. I mean, who needs four point two litres, a big shiny bonnet, and whatever else it is? I don't rush around desperately helping people, and I don't give all my bread away to everybody. But the argument we are constantly up against is that you can't have the luxury of socialist principles and compassionate feelings for people who are less well off than you are, and still have five grand in the bank, or whatever. We're forever wrestling about that."

"I guess Dark Side changed everything," I said.

"It sure did. I now have more than enough money to buy a house. So, what do I do with all the money? You go through this thing where you think of all the good you could do with it by giving it away. But, in the end, you keep it."

I wondered how it must feel to earn so much money almost overnight. What would I do?

Nick was quiet. Staring a thousand-yard stare. Was he thinking the same?

Roger switched to a more philosophical mood.

"You know Matt, maybe some Hindus would disagree but, other than golf, you only get one shot at life. You've got to make choices based on whatever moral, philosophical or political position you adopt. Those choices are influenced by political considerations, by money and by the dark side of all our natures. That's what the bloody album is all about, isn't it? You get the chance to make the world a lighter or a darker place in some small way."

Dark Side Of The Moon had gone gold in both the UK and the US. Any fool could hear it was Pink Floyd's best and most coherent album to date. The powerful songs captured people's imagination and the brilliant lyrics had depth and a resonance people could easily relate to. There was not a single weak moment or song on the record.

"You must be incredibly proud to have made your mark with such a magnificent piece of music," I said as Roger took another swig from his pint.

"I am. It's special. When we finished it, I took the tape home and played it to Judy. She burst into tears when she'd finished listening to it. I wasn't surprised, I think it's emotionally and musically very moving. It strikes a chord with people."

"Including your bank manager," Nick said dryly, still gazing towards the 18th green.

"We'd have danced naked around Shaftesbury Memorial Fountain if we'd thought it would sell records," Waters laughed. "We needed this one to be a success."

"And it will make recording the next one a lot easier, I suppose."

Roger's expression suddenly tensed.

"Are you kidding me? It makes it a hell of a lot more difficult!"

Seeing the puzzled look on my face, he relaxed a bit.

"How do you top a success like that?" he explained. "The pressure is ridiculous. We're working like dogs but have nothing to show for it. Everything we try ends up crawling to a dead end."

"Dead end?"

"We're searching for a hook, a theme, a sound, something but getting nowhere. It's incredibly frustrating."

"Lack of inspiration?"

"That and a lack of commitment. We spend days in the studio doing absolutely nothing. That's when everyone's around and not playing squash or shooting at dart boards with an air rifle. When I'm in the studio, I am there to do something. If not, I'd rather be somewhere else. I'm there to work."

"A lack of focus, then," Nick interjected.

"I know we're all in relationships now," Roger continued. "And we're still tired from touring. But, yeah, we need to focus. I want a new album that hangs together conceptually, and I want it to be an homage to Syd. I feel pretty miserable about what happened and it would be good to get that across: a kind of heartfelt expression of my sadness. I'm working on one song about Syd. The rest is about feelings of absence. Which is kind of fitting given the trouble I'm having getting everybody back to work again."

"Is there a deadline?" I asked.

"No. At least, not yet. They think I'm pushy and forcing my ideas onto them. But surely it's better to move in my direction than to continue without any direction or ideas at all. It's not as if the four of us are together because we all think and feel the same way, or because we all love each other and are working towards a common cause or better music or anything like that. We're together because we all like the security of being in a band. Not to forget the economic security now we have a number one selling record. The truth is, we fight a lot while going nowhere. The problems are endless and I'm getting pretty fed up with it all."

"So, guys," Nick said on a lighter note, "how about Bayern Munich beating Atletico Madrid? Did you see the match, last night? 4-0! Those bloody Germans were relentless!"

His timing was perfect. No need to spoil a good day with bad vibes about work. He signalled the waiter.

"Can we have three more beers, please? These gentlemen are thirsty and in desperate need of some inspiration."

25
DON'T LEAVE ME NOW

Home, December 21, 1975

The sheets and blankets were a mess, but we were happy lying entangled beneath them. A lazy Sunday morning, rain pouring down outside and nothing else to do other than enjoy each other's company. I jumped out of bed, turned the heater up a few notches, made toast and coffee, put Wish You Were Here on the record player and snuggled back in.

"You still listen to that band?" she asked, taking a sip of her coffee.

"Yes, I do. You won't believe how much they've changed. Not sure if we can call each other friends, but I've got to know them pretty well over the last few years."

"Seriously?"

"Seriously!"

My reunion with Carly came as a complete surprise. She'd seen my name in the music mag and written to me via the editorial office. They'd sent the letter on to my studio address. In it, she reminisced about the time we'd spent together in Amsterdam and how she regretted leaving me behind in the Paradiso. She'd since moved to the UK and asked if I fancied meeting up. As I wasn't seeing anybody else, and curious to find out how she was doing seven years on, I invited her over for dinner. She looked even prettier than I remembered, and I found myself lost in her bright green eyes all over again. One thing had led to another. And here we were, the very next morning, having breakfast in bed and listening to the band that had brought us back together.

"What is it that attracts you to their music, Matt? It's not as if you can dance to it."

"You've never seen me dance," I quipped blithely. "Pink Floyd touches my soul. It's some kind of spiritual thing, I can't really put my finger on it. Their music moves me in lots of ways. It brings me comfort and joy. It lifts me up when I'm down, and it puts things into perspective when I'm lost. I like the melodic structure of their songs, the harmonies, the rhythms, the great guitar lines and the keyboards. Some early, experimental stuff I don't care for, but their more recent albums are very, very dear to me. Want some more coffee?"

"Yes, please! What are they like? Not as musicians, I mean as people?"

I got out of bed and returned with the jug of coffee.

"How can I best describe them," I said, mulling over what I knew in my head. "I suppose you could say they're very British. They're quite reserved and have a detached, wicked line of humour that is sometimes even cruel. They throw out biting gibes like missiles. Work-wise, they're a very tight-knit band. Socially, less so. They don't really mix outside work."

"Is there a leader, a boss?"

"I think Roger views himself as being the alpha male," I laughed. "Especially since he now writes most of the material. People think he's some kind of dictator, but although he can be a bit pushy, he's actually a very humorous guy. And being the band's conceptualist and lyricist, he's a big picture thinker. David's more introspective. The educated, level-headed, well-spoken diplomat type. Richard is quite shy, but he's a very talented musician. It's Richard that provides Pink Floyd with its musical soul. Because he's a bit absent-minded though, his importance for the overall sound of the band is often overlooked."

"And Nick? He's the drummer, right?" Carly asked.

"Yeah. Nick Mason. Nick's the peacekeeper. But they're all fairly private, but not ridiculously so. Now I come to think about it, I'd say Pink Floyd is a band with two faces. One minute they're squabbling, the next, they're giving each other the silent treatment. Either way, they can be an intimidating bunch of people. Still, I enjoy their company and music."

We're just two lost souls, swimming in a fishbowl, year after year...

I heard David Gilmour singing through the speakers. How I loved those lyrics.

Outside, the rain had turned to snow. We looked at the flakes softly falling to the ground. Memories of Syd Barrett floated by.

"Do you remember me telling you about how I met Syd, Pink Floyd's original singer and guitarist, when I was on holiday in Ibiza?" I asked Carly after a while.

"Um, I think so. On the ferry, right?"

"Yeah. In fact, his actual name's not Syd, it's Roger. They say he was brilliant, but also a bit of an addict and he sort of short-circuited his brain. Apparently, he's gone into isolation and won't see or talk to anybody other than his family anymore. I've been thinking about him a lot lately."

"Why's that, Matt?"

"I met Nick for a couple of pints in the city the other day

and he told me this incredibly sad story. Apparently, the band had been mixing a song for the new album, the one we're listening to now, in fact, and Syd had turned up. They didn't know who it was at first. This guy in a raincoat just crashed in unannounced and started walking about the studio. He was fat with a bald head and shaved-off eyebrows, and they thought he must be a member of the crew. When they realised it was their former bandmate, they were shocked. Nick said that Roger had even been in tears. The weirdest thing was that the song they were mixing was inspired by Syd. It was all about him."

Shine On You Crazy Diamond filled the room.

"Oh, that's awfully sad," Carly said, softly.

"It is. He was pretty fogged out, but they managed to speak with him. It turned out he was still living in London and when he read somewhere the band was working down at the Abbey Road Studios, he just decided to go and take a look. Roger, Rick and David had worked on Syd's two solo albums and it was only a year since they'd last seen him. Nick said they were devastated by how much he'd changed. In the end, Syd just left as suddenly as he'd appeared."

"It must have freaked everyone out."

"Yeah, I think it did it. It certainly brought back a lot of memories, and not all of them good. I think the band feels a guilty that while they're busy being successful and earning lots of money, Syd has been left in the lurch. Some people say they're heartless and selfish for not looking after Syd's mental wellbeing. But I don't think they are. Roger, Nick and David helped Syd a lot with his solo albums. I think he gets all his royalties as well."

"They've left their former friend to sort his problems alone."

"I'm not sure if Syd actually wanted help. It must have been a nightmare to work with him. How do you deal with a friend who's clearly losing his mind, but you've no idea why or what's causing it? It must have been so frustrating to work with somebody who refused to sing his parts, deliberately detuned his guitar in the middle of a song or simply didn't show up for gigs. He was wrecking the band just when they needed everyone to pull together and give it their all. They did everything they could to keep Syd in the band. That's why David was brought in. He was there to back up Syd."

"And all this because of some bad trips?"

"I don't know. Maybe the drugs pushed Syd over the edge. Syd was a bordering genius. They say there's a fine line between genius and insanity. Maybe LSD erased the line. Maybe it's something in his genes? Who knows? I don't think there's anything wrong with seeking the edge of your limits. It's how we grow and expand our possibilities. But how do you know when you've reached the edge? How do you know to turn back before it's too late? Scary stuff."

"Have you ever taken any drugs?" Carly asked bluntly.

"I've smoked a few joints. But it's not really my thing. I get nothing done when I'm stoned, it drains all the energy out of me. Don't like cigarettes, either. I'm more a beer and wine kind of guy. You?"

"I won't touch any of that," she said. "I've seen it destroy the lives of too many people around me. One of my best friends overdosed on heroine a couple of months ago. I'd no idea she was a junkie. And then, suddenly, I'm standing next to her grave saying goodbye. She was only 27."

"Sorry to hear that."

"Are any of the guys in the band married?" Carly asked, changing the subject.

"David and Ginger got married this summer. They held their reception at the Abbey Road Studios."

"That's not a very romantic setting for a wedding reception."

"These are not very romantic musicians ..."

"And the other three?"

"Nick and Lindy have been married since back in the sixties. Richard and Juliette, too. Roger and Judy are getting divorced, though. No idea why. I've only just heard."

We both stared at the ceiling, listening to the dying seconds of Shine On You Crazy Diamond.

"Isn't it time we moved in together?" I asked.

27
HAVE A CIGAR

Wembley Empire Pool, London, March 19, 1977

Carly had suddenly left me a few weeks ago. She'd fallen for some other guy she met on the train to London, packed her things into bags and boxes and drove off. As simple and as cold as that. I was gutted. First came the questions, then the anger and frustration and, finally, the despair as I drowned myself in liquid sorrow and self-pity. I was off radar for five days. When it was over, I still didn't have any answers, but I did have an angry boss and the worst hangover ever.

I desperately needed a breather. There was only one place I knew I could really get some quality time with myself, only one place I felt completely at home. For me, being in a crowded concert hall is like being alone in an empty room with nobody to tell you what to do or what to think. Put me in the middle of hundreds and thousands of people and it doesn't matter who the band is, what kind of music they play or how famous they are. The effect is always the same: I feel safe and sound. Whether it is an old church filled with spaced-out heads or a stadium packed with music fanatics, the minute the music starts, my head- and heartaches vanish, sadness and sorrow cease to exist, and everything that feels bad, sad, or negative disappears. There is only happiness and joy, curiosity, wonder and excitement. Even if the show sucks, there is no other place on earth I would rather be.

As luck would have it, it turned out Pink Floyd was playing at London's Empire Pool five nights in a row. I'd not seen them since the US and Canada tour in '73, and after our little golfing adventure, the only contact I'd had with Roger was via the occasional telephone call. He was almost never at home, so I usually ended up talking to Carolyne, the girl Roger had married in 1976.

I called her up. She was really sweet, and after checking with Roger, called Steve O'Rourke's office and asked to put me on the list for the fifth night. A gracious gesture for someone I'd had never actually met in person. "Roger said you're one of the good guys," she'd replied when I thanked her, "and you're welcome to say hello after the show."

▪ ▪ ▪

When I arrived at the huge Wembley Empire, the place was alive with excitement and anticipation. This was the last of five 12.000-seat sell-out shows. The production was the biggest the band had ever undertaken. They were now nothing less than superstars. It was good to see some old friends. I stopped to say hello to lighting technician Robin Murray, PA man Robbie Williams, production manager Arthur Max, and tour manager Mick Kluczynski, who everyone addressed as 'The Pole'. After five nights they were a bit strung out, but the mood was good. As usual when they played London, the stakes were just that bit higher and the guest list a little longer. There was double the amount of gear on stage as there had been four years ago and there seemed to be twice the number of crews and other people involved. I also noticed security was much tighter too, and that there was already a small army of photographers waiting in front of the stage.

People were still coming in when, at eight o'clock sharp, the lights went out and the sounds of bleating sheep were played from tape. Ah, yes, Sheep. Pink Floyd had recently released a new LP called Animals. It was an altogether more direct album than Dark Side and Wish You Were Here. The political theme, raw rhythms, and edgy melodies produced a sound that was darkly confrontational, soulful, but also a little tongue in cheek.

Some lovely organ work from Richard Wright set the tone, and as the darkened stage suddenly flooded with light, the band was in full swing. Dave Gilmour was on lead guitar of course, but, to my surprise, Roger Waters was playing rhythm guitar and a guy I'd never seen before was on bass. As David edged into a great solo, brilliant flashes of light sprayed the band from pneumatic telescopic cranes that slowly rose into the air on either side of the stage. What a majestic opening!

After a thundering applause, Roger Waters switched to acoustic guitar to give a tender rendering of Pigs On The Wing Part 1, then the band launched into Dogs, with David taking lead vocals. They played a longer version than on the record, and it was sublime. The concert was only just underway, but already there was a very electric energy bouncing back and forth between the audience and stage; a wild feeling and much more intense than I'd experienced before. It was difficult to conceive this was the same fledgling combo I'd seen perform their psychedelic jams in Amsterdam. Here, they were a band of masterful superstars that had conquered the world. The whole packed out stadium was at their feet and I was jubilant.

Being accepted into their inner circle was immensely important to me. I felt grateful and more than a little proud. Not because the band had made it big or was idolised by so many people, but because Pink Floyd had gone where few artists had gone before and now reigned musically supreme.

An enormous inflatable man appeared out of nowhere to the right of the stage, then a smaller child figure and then a mother on a blow-up couch. Floating, they moved until the man was hovering over his 'family' like an ominous bird. They deflated somewhere in the middle of the second verse, puffed up again, and as Roger brought the song to a crashing conclusion, they finally collapsed into a crumbled heap behind the stage.

Next up was Pigs On The Wing part 2, followed by the husky snorts that signalled the intro to Pigs (Three Different Ones). The spotlights on the gantries moved from Rick to Roger and Dave, flooding each in a column of light as they played their parts. Roger's vocals were sharper, more vicious than on the song's studio counterpart. I was blown away all over again by the power of the sound and the full venue acoustics. My body filled with the music and I felt as if I was being lifted ten feet from the floor.

A few minutes later, a mist of dry ice billowed up from either side of the stage. The band moved into an extended instrumental passage and with the new guy ripping an amazing guitar solo, a giant pink pig trundled into view. The huge honker flew over the audience, scanning us with its searchlight eyes, and exited on the other side of the stage as the song ended. We rocked the arena with our applause until a smiling Roger announced the band was taking a twenty-minute break.

The house lights came on with a pop, and it brought us back to reality. Looking around, I was amazed by how many people were smiling despite the brutal interruption. Along with a few others, I sat myself down on the floor. Alone amidst thousands of strangers, my thoughts drifted back to Carly. Unlooked for, a line from the Fleetwood Mac's Dreams drifted into my mind: 'Thunder only happens when it's raining, players only love you when they're playing.' No idea why, but I did really like the record. They'd released it a few months back, and it's not often you like every single track on a new album at the first spin. Obviously, Rumours had nestled itself into my brain and I smiled. Funny how music and words make an impact without you knowing it. I wondered if the lyrics were trying to tell me something, but then quickly put the idea that Stevie Nicks was sending me secret messages out of my mind.

Sitting there in my musical cocoon, I realised how much I was not looking forward to going back to work after the weekend. My dream of becoming a full-time rock journalist had been quashed when it became clear that writing about music would never generate enough income to cover the rent. I'd also become disillusioned with the whole music industry when I found out that being a successful reporter had little to do with a love of music, or even with being able to write a good read. It was all about knowing the right people. And about kissing a lot of ass to be first in line whenever the new releases and exclusive interviews were handed out. My music journalist colleagues were little better. They professed to detest the music industry and would fulminate against record label bosses at the pre-show hangouts, the backstage parties and in many editorial rants. But the next cool, all-expenses-paid press trips they were only too eager to accept. I also hated how they would drool over their latest 'hip and happening' artists one minute, only to throw them under the bus as boring has-beens the next. I had never liked the in-crowd music scene, and I probably never will. Hence my current job as an assistant publisher. Which I didn't much like either.

The lights went out, again. It was time to stop feeling sorry for myself and I stood up. As the band emerged from clouds of dry ice and broke into the unmistakable, classic intro to Shine On You Crazy Diamond, a big circular screen showed a surreal film of a man, then a beach. It doesn't matter how often I hear this song, it's always epic and it always moves me to the bone. Especially since I'd once met the person who the song was all about. I pinked away a little tear as Dick Parry played a brilliant solo on his sax.

More surreal film sequences accompanied a fierce rendition of Welcome To The Machine, segueing into a slightly altered version of Have A Cigar with Nick's penetrating drums, Roger's distinctive vocals and blazes of light from the telescopic towers flying across the stage. As the song reached its end, a transistor radio rose from the stage and played the 'switching channels' sound. We heard the first smooth acoustic guitar licks of Wish You Were Here.

"We're two lost souls, swimming in a fishbowl...". Sentimental memories of Carly and I flashed through my mind, but the windy opening of Shine On You Crazy Diamond Parts 6-9 blew them clear away. David played a mean lap steel guitar, but the real hero was Rick Wright, whose keyboard sounds took the packed arena to places we'd never been or seen before. Goosebumps and a huge glass-mirrored, rotating sunburst ball were all part of the deal.

The ear-splitting ovation seemed to last forever. As an encore, Pink Floyd played Money, and flooded the whole stage with dancing, dazzling light. The extended version of the song seemed to last forever, but eventually Nick slowed the tempo down until, with a final crash, the magnificent night came to an end.

Some were trying to take it all in, others strolled towards the exits. We were all a bit dazed by the overload on our senses. After a while, euphoria took over and people started to laugh, yell, sing, hug, shake hands, pat each other on the shoulders. I even saw a couple of fans in tears. We had witnessed something special, and we all knew it.

I felt like a ball of pent-up energy and emotions and wanted to run, skip and jump like a small kid. I couldn't wait to tell the band how much I'd enjoyed the show and only just managed to restrain myself as I passed the security guards to reach the dressing rooms.

▪ ▪ ▪

The lively and upbeat mood of the concert hall was oddly missing backstage. The place was pretty crowded but the atmosphere was more tense than buzzing. And what an eclectic gathering of people they were: film stars, tv personalities, musicians, men in suits, a bunch of hippies, some hell's angels and girls, lots of girls. Most of them were in their teens and early twenties, some all dressed up and looking drop dead gorgeous, others looked like they could do with a good meal and a bit of sun.

One guy with a ponytail, flip flops, and a small duffel bag was openly selling drugs to three people wearing VIP-passes. He was making no effort to conceal his trade and was dealing his little paper packages as if it was perfectly normal. Looking around, I saw that the band's dressing rooms were still closed. There was no sign of any wives or family, either and I guessed they'd probably all been at the first few shows. Concert number five was obviously reserved for a guest list of a different sort.

"We call them the puppies," somebody next to me said, obviously having noticed me staring at a group of four young girls. I turned my head and recognised the speaker as one of the crew. I couldn't remember his name though.

"Puppies?" I asked.

"Yeah. They're probably all underage, but they follow us around everywhere," the roadie said, yelling to be heard over the noise of animated conversations and laughter.

I walked over to a long line of tables spread with plates of food and an assortment of drinks. Seeing a few open bottles of Champaign, I poured myself a bubbly drink.

Two guys were chatting in the corner of the room. Recognising one of them as the new guy I'd seen playing bass and guitar, I waited until the other person left, then walked over and introduced myself.

"Hi, I'm Matt."

"Hello Matt, I'm Snowy."

"Great to meet you, Snowy! I just wanted to let you know how impressed I was with your performance tonight. Like you'd been playing with them for years."

"Thanks! That's nice of you to say. Really appreciate it."

"You're welcome. Have you played with any other bands? I'd like to hear more of your music."

"Not any bands you'd know. I've played with Peter Green, though. You may have heard his name before; he was the original guitar player with Fleetwood Mac."

"Yeah, a brilliant musician. Didn't he write Oh Well and Albatross?"

"Yes, that's right, he did. I love those songs! He wrote Santana's Black Magic Woman, too, although few people know that."

The noise suddenly grew louder and out of the corner of my eye, I saw Nick and Roger enter the room. Snowy briefly turned his head to see what was going on. His band mates were surrounded by women, a bizarre and uncharacteristic sight that made us both smile."

"Do you mind me asking how you ended up with playing with the Floyd?"

"That was a very strange experience! I've always considered myself to be a straight up and down blues man. If there's no blues in it, I don't even listen. Anyway, last year, somebody told me Pink Floyd was looking for a second guitarist for a tour and recommended I ring the band's manager. At the time, I knew nothing about Pink Floyd and was probably the only guy in England not to have heard Dark Side Of The Moon. That's how out of the loop I was. Then, when I found out about them and realised they didn't play blues, I thought we probably wouldn't work well together. What would be the point? But I called anyway, and they invited me to audition."

"How did it go?"

"Well, I went down to the studio where they were recording, they asked me a few questions and then Rog told Dave to take me to the office and explain what the gig was all about. That was it, basically. Dave told me what they wanted me to play and asked me if I wanted the gig. I said OK but when I suggested we play something, a jam maybe, he just said: 'You wouldn't be here if you couldn't play, would you?' and that was the end of my audition. They sent me some of their records to listen to and, to my surprise, I liked what I heard. Some of their music is actually pretty bluesy."

"You seemed to enjoy yourself on stage tonight."

"I did. It's fantastic to play all that iconic music, I had a great time. I get that there's something going on between Roger and David, some tension or whatever, but I try to keep out of all that."

I nodded to show I knew what he was referring to.

"It's a completely unique experience for me," Snowy continued. "I've only played in clubs before and now suddenly I'm doing these huge venues in front of thousands of fans all going bonkers over Pink Floyd. It's hard to realise that I'm playing with such a successful band. I guess my head's still stuck in my blues."

"You're an excellent match, Snowy."

"Thanks. I think you're right."

"Will you be recording with them as well?"

"I already have," Snowy said, laughing.

"I went to the studio again later," he continued. "They were recording Pigs On The Wing and Roger said: 'Well, as you're here, you might as well play something.' So I played some guitar. When the album was done, they used my version of the song on the 8-track tape album release."

"Why didn't they use it on the LP?"

"You should ask them. I think it had something to do with royalties. You won't hear me complain. I'm happy to be here. Anyway, it was nice talking to you, Matt."

Having politely dismissed me, Snowy turned to some other people who were waiting to talk with him. I wandered back to the refreshments table and was pouring myself another paper cup of Champaign, when somebody bumped into me. Nearly dropping a full bottle of Moët, I heard Nick Mason chuckle.

"I see you're enjoying yourself?" he said with the usual twinkle in his eyes.

"I can say the same about you guys," I said, glancing towards the women circling Roger.

"How did you like the show?" Nick asked, ignoring the quip.

"I thought it was absolutely brilliant. I couldn't take my eyes off the drummer," I said. "He was the only one moving on stage. He and the inflatables, that is."

Nick grinned and saw me staring over at the groupies again, who were zeroing in on the crew and the rest of the band, especially now David and Rick had joined the party. Taking me gently by the arm, Nick steered me towards a quieter part of the room.

"I'd appreciate it if you didn't write about this sort of stuff, Matt," he said, lowering his voice to a conspiratorial whisper. "This being the last of our London gigs, we're having a bit of a party. When the tour is over, we want to be sure we have families to go back to. We know we can trust you."

"Sure, Nick. No worries. When tonight is over, I want to have some friends to go back to, too."

Nick smiled and gave me a military salute. "Thanks, old chap."

"You're a hardworking band with a hardworking crew. I'm sure nobody minds you all blowing off some steam."

"Being on the road for months on end is stressful on many different levels. The production is growing exponentially the scale of the new venues asks a great deal of our crew, including some real mountaineering skills. One special team, we call them the 'quad squad', has to lug our quad speakers right up to the furthest and highest corners of these huge stadiums and venues, like Wembley, for example."

"Snowy just told me he'd done some recording with you guys, but that it had only made the 8-track release. Was that a conscious decision?" I asked curiously.

"Hmm, I don't know, to be honest. Much of the material for Animals already existed as a bunch of songs Roger had previously written. Towards the end of recording, Roger also wrote the two Pigs On The Wing pieces to open and close the album. That started a whole discussion about how we share publishing royalties since Roger now had two additional tracks to his name."

"Why is that a problem?" I asked.

"It's to do with the fact that the publishing companies pay for a specific number of tracks on an album, and if you don't have that many tracks, they simply cut the payment. We included a certain number of tracks on the album for good reason. It's why some songs are divided into parts 1, 2 and 3. The only problem then was how to divide the royalties amongst the band."

"Snowy's bit is not on the album because you didn't want to share the royalties?"

"No, not really. It's more a result of how we worked on splitting songs. Brian, our engineer, was on a break, so Roger and I assumed engineering duties, but we somehow erased the guitar solo David had just finished. That's when Snowy turned up at the studio, Roger wanted him to have a go at the Pigs On The Wing solo. But when the track was split in two, we didn't need his solo and it only appeared on the full 8-track cartridge version."

"I really enjoy listening to Animals. It's a much more straightforward album."

"I totally agree. There was a bigger group commitment than on Wish You Were Here. Maybe it's because we now operate our own studio and mixing was a relatively painless process. But maybe it's just that we've got better and quicker at what we do."

"Well, you better quickly re-join your friends then," I said, excusing the drummer who seemed to be getting a little impatient.

Nick smiled, nodded and walked over to a group of people he appeared to know. By now, the full road crew had joined the festivities and the sound of talking and laughing had gone up another few notches. The oddly charged atmosphere I'd felt when I arrived had gone and been replaced by a wild aftershow party. In desperate need of a leak, I strode to the toilets at the end of a corridor. The first door I tried was locked. The sounds coming from it were definitely not from one person. I shook my head and tried the next door and when it opened went in. The sounds from the adjoining lavatory were much louder now, and whoever was in there was having a lot of fun.

Back in the green room, things were also getting a little out of hand. Some crew members were throwing the contents of the salad bar at each other. As people realised this was probably the start of an all-out food fight, everybody looked for safety elsewhere. The talking and laughing continued as if nothing out of the ordinary was going on, but the roadies were all chasing each other, yelling and cursing. When a piece of flying celery narrowly missed hitting me on the head, I decided it was time for me to beat a retreat. I triend to cut a corner and bumped into Roger Waters.

"Matt! The missus told me you were coming to see us. Are we having fun?"

"We are. I really enjoyed the show. Best one I've seen so far. You guys were in exceptional form tonight."

"Thanks. Coming from you, that really means a lot."

"You've got a great concept there with Animals," I said. "I guess it leans on Orwell and Animal Farm?"

"Of course," Roger replied. "It's quite obvious, isn't it? It's a kind of cartoon sketch. Animals that represent traits of human behaviour."

"It's powerful stuff!" I replied at the top of my voice, trying to make my voice hear above the noise of the party. "And chilling at the same time."

"Glad you like it. I've had the idea in the back of my mind for years. The rest of the band had little to offer. Dave came up with some ideas, but I consider this mainly my brainchild.

So, what are you up to these days?"

"Um..." I hesitated. "Not much really. I'm pretty fed up with my job and my girlfriend has just left me. Nothing to worry about and nothing I can't survive. Seeing you guys play cheered me up. What more can I ask than to return home happy."

"Well, the least you can do is enjoy the party. Here, grab a beer."

Roger got two beers from a bucket filled with ice, popped the caps, handed one to me and hit his bottle with mine.

"Cheers, Matt. To all the pigs in the world and to better times ahead."

Roger gave me a pat on the shoulder and walked off to entertain the other guests.

For a minute I wasn't sure whether to feel angry or sorry for myself. I'd just bared my soul to someone I deeply admired, and his only response was to hand me a beer and walk away? Backstage was probably not the best setting for an intimate conversation. It was not my party after all. What an idiot I am, I thought. Who wants to hear about someone's personal tragedy at their post-show party? No wonder he walked. Feeling ashamed of my stupidity, I looked around for some familiar faces or at least a place to sit. After a long night, my legs and feet were killing me.

Before I could sit down, I first had to avoid the crew who by now were chasing each other with fire extinguishers. None of them had gone off, but the threat of being covered in white foam caused a lot of yelling as everyone tried to get out of their way. I ended up seeking refuge in one of the dressing rooms. Finding an empty couch, I plonked myself down. Leaning back and drinking my beer, I realised this was probably the closest to good old-fashioned rock 'n' roll a Pink Floyd concert was ever going to get. Looking at all the happy people in the crowded room, I relaxed and soaked up the atmosphere. Who cares about a fuckin' heartache when you've got beer, vegetables and fire extinguishers? I smiled and decided to indulge myself with the festivities of the rich and famous a little longer. This party wasn't over, yet.

27
IS THERE ANYBODY OUT THERE?

Hospital & home, July 10, 1977

I wasn't particularly fond of disco, but I had a soft spot for funk, blues and soul. Chic, Marvin Gaye, Johnny Guitar Watson, Stevie Wonder, they all struck a chord, which was a little strange for someone who'd recently bought albums by Supertramp, Peter Gabriel and Jethro Tull. Funk was about groovy rhythms, soul could make your heart melt, while blues made it cry. I had some popular music among the prog stuff in my record collection, but I must admit I mostly listened to it on the radio.

I was probably the only one around who noted and appreciated Hot Chocolate's So You Win Again coming out of the radio in the hospital's waiting area. An uncomplicated pop song with killer vocals and heaps of soul. Errol Brown's warm words filled the room where I was waiting for the doctor's OK. So You Win Again, what an ironic title for a loser with his left arm in plaster, bruised ribs and several now thoroughly cleansed wounds. They should have examined my head, too. I couldn't have been more stupid; the car had rolled three times and come to a halt in a roadside ditch. A friendly man had found me lying beside the car after I'd apparently climbed out by myself. Not that I remembered any of it. I'd had a few too many, that much I knew. The man had brought me to a nearby hospital, later claiming I'd refused to allow him to call an ambulance. I wondered if my car was still in the ditch.

"Mr Hallander?"

The doctor I was waiting for introduced himself as Anderson and gave me a brief but firm handshake and a rather stern look. Both of which made me cringe.

"You are a very lucky man."

"I know."

"You know? Then you should also know we should notify the police, especially given your test results. But we will not do that. I figure you've learned your lesson. It's far too busy for a Sunday, and I am not in the mood for any extra paperwork. If you'd like to follow me, the admin department will make an appointment for you to have the cast removed in about six weeks' time. I suggest that in future you be more careful and sensible when driving a car, Mr Hallander."

"I will. And thank you, Doctor Anderson."

As I walked out through the hospital doors, I saw a pale, bruised face reflecting in the windows.

▪ ▪ ▪

After I'd paid the cab fare, I unlocked the front door and went straight for the fridge. I took out some ice to put on my left shoulder and a single malt to ease the pain in the rest of my body. I then carefully lay down on the coach and put my glass down on the small table next to me. My hand was trembling as reality finally kicked in.

Girlfriend gone, car gone, no work, no money in the bank and a wreck on the sofa, I guess this is meant by hitting rock bottom. I was tired and my body was aching too much to feel any grief or sorrow. I popped a few painkillers from the strip, took a good gulp of whisky, made a mental note to find out what had happened to the car or what's left of it, and dozed off.

It was the phone that woke me up. I'd lost my watch in either the car or the hospital and had no idea what time it was. I tried to get up, but was immediately regretting it. My chest was hurting like mad and my head was pounding and protesting to the loud ring.

"Hello?"

"Matt?"

"Yes," I mumbled, "who's this?"

"It's Roger."

"Roger who?" I asked, still fuzzy from sleeping, the meds and booze.

"Roger Waters, you idiot."

A shock of recognition whipped through my body, causing yet another gush of pain. Roger calling me? That was a first. But why?

"Oh, hey, Roger. Sorry I didn't recognise your voice. I must have dozed off. Still feel a bit drowsy. How are you doing, man?"

"How am I doing? I should be asking you that. I heard you'd had an accident."

"Yeah, I rolled the car trying to avoid a deer crossing the road. Ended up in some ditch."

"You OK?"

"Sort of. Broke my left arm. Lots of bruises, including a bruised ego. And a wrecked car. How did you find out, anyway?"

"You remember our production manager, Mick Kluczynski?"

"Yes, I believe I do."

"It was him who took you to the hospital. He phoned yesterday to tell me what had happened."

"Really? I thought he looked familiar," I lied.

"He said you were really out of it. Obviously in pain, talking a lot of gibberish. And smelling of alcohol, he'd said. Mick saved your arse by not involving the local authorities."

"Oh, wow. Can't thank him enough for that. What a real class act he is. I'll call him when I feel better."

"You should be more careful, Matt." Roger Waters sounded like my dad. Concerned.

"I will, thanks. I think I've learned my lesson," I said, the words of the doctor still resonating in my head.

I looked at the empty glass. Something had got to change. Only not right now. But I had Roger Waters on the phone. Why would he care?

"I thought you guys were touring the US?"

"We flew back last Friday."

"How did it go?"

I heard Roger exhale. A long, weary, frustrated sigh.

"I don't want to talk about it, really."

"That doesn't sound too good. Sure you don't want to tell me about it?"

"It's all so frustrating," he sighed, again.

"What is?"

"Everything. I'm so fucking tired of all this shit."

"What kind of shit, Rog?"

I had never called him 'Rog' before.

"I spat somebody in the face."

"You did what?"

"Spat him in the face. I was on stage and there was this guy in the front row shouting and screaming all the way through everything. I called him over, he climbed up the storm netting and when he got close enough, I spat him in the face."

"You spat in some guy's face because he was screaming during one of your gigs?" I asked in disbelieve.

"I'm afraid I did. In Montreal during the last show of the tour. I was really shocked with myself. But it has also got me thinking. Look, it's not something I'm proud off."

"Any idea what made you do it?"

"Not really, but I'm fed up playing to these large audiences. I remember when we used to play for, say, 3500 people and you could hear a pin drop. Everybody sat and listened. Those were the days, Matt. Now, in these football stadiums, they're all shouting and screaming, getting drunk... What the fuck is wrong with people? And then the fireworks... Some idiots let off fireworks while we were playing. I'm not sure how to deal with this going forward, but it can't go on like this."

"I can understand that losing the intimacy of performing can be frustrating."

"Well," Roger continued, "it's more complicated than that. You're right, playing music to an audience that isn't listening is no fun, but I also feel we're losing control. This thing is becoming too big, Matt. It's not growing over our heads or anything, but the feeling of constantly having to keep on your toes, not to fuck up and not to get fucked over, is sometimes just too much. A couple of days before the last show in Montreal we did Soldiers' Field in Chicago. Before the gig started, I was standing on the bleachers at the back of the stage looking down at the audience when Steve had come up. Standing beside me, he asked to go guess how many people there were and when I said I didn't know, told me there were sixty-three thousand. I've done enough big shows to know what sixty thousand people looks like. I looked down again and said 'no way', there's at least eighty thousand, if not a hundred thousand down there.' Steve said he would check. The box office told him it was sold out to an audience of sixty-three thousand. We rented a helicopter, a photographer and an attorney and photographed it all from the air. It turned out there were ninety-five thousand people at the gig. So where was the ticket money for the thirty-two thousand extra people? That's six hundred and forty thousand dollars!"

"Man, that sucks!" I replied.

"Yeah, it does. It's an alienating experience doing these shows. It's exceedingly difficult to perform when people are whistling and shouting and screaming and throwing things and hitting each other and crashing about and letting off fireworks. But the weirdest thing is that it's a situation we've created ourselves through our own greed, you know? The only real reason for playing large venues is to make money."

"Does the rest of the band feel the same?"

"I don't fuckin' care. David is probably still pissed at me for spitting at the guy. He didn't want to play the last encore of the tour. My guess is he's as fed up with it as I am. We all miss playing the smaller venues. I also think there's a fair amount of boredom involved. The bigger the gigs, the smaller the cocoon becomes we're living in. Apart from hanging around in the hotel, watching tv and the occasional golf match, there's not much else to do when you're on the road."

"What are you up to now, then?"

"I desperately need some time off. To get away from everything."

"You need a holiday."

"I need a sabbatical!"

"What are you going to do?"

"I'm interested in some properties in the south of France. Me and Carolyn are thinking of buying a house down there. I'm sure that'll keep me occupied for a while."

"Sounds cool. If you need someone to clean the pool or do the gardening, give me a call."

"We need you to get that arm healed first."

"You're right. I've got to get my life back on track."

"What have you been up to, Matt, while we were away selling out stadiums, making millions and spitting at our fans? Apart from crashing your car, that is."

Surprised by the sudden, unexpected, and uncharacteristic interest in my personal life, I needed a few seconds to formulate an answer.

"You see... there's not much going on right now... Actually, I feel miserable. My girlfriend has left me, and I've quit my job at the newspaper."

"Good!"

"Good?"

"I've got a job for you."

"A job?"

"Don't worry, I don't want you to be our pool cleaner."

"You remember Nick Sedgwick, right?"

"Your golfing buddy."

"Correct. Well, he's written a book about a trip he came on with me and Judy to Greece. The three of us spent the entire summer there together, and Nick witnessed the beginnings of the end of my first marriage. That autumn, he also travelled with the band on The Dark Side Of The Moon tour, including the subsequent American leg. He recorded a lot of the conversations that went on and documented the tour's progress. I've read the manuscript and quite liked it. It's an honest story and none of us comes out of it particularly well. Not surprisingly, the rest of the band doesn't want it to be published. It will probably never see the light of day, but it got me thinking. I want somebody to document my personal take on being in the band, the music industry, politics."

I felt a sense of excitement mixed with a great deal of disbelief. I took a deep breath.

"Why me? Why now?" I asked.

"From what I've heard, you're a talented writer and I like somebody around who I know. And trust. You know the band and they know you."

"But why do you want to write a book now?" I asked again.

"I'm not saying that this band has run its course, but I feel we're at a crossroad here. If the last tour made one thing clear, it's that I don't want to carry on like this. Something has got to happen. Something has got to change. I'm not sure what. Right now, the only thing I'm certain about is that we need a change of perspective. And either the band and management follow me on this, or I'm out."

"And where exactly do I, and writing a book, fit in to all this?"

"I want you to talk to the band about how we've changed as individuals and as a unit. What effect does money, success, the stadium shows, the immense and still growing scale of what we do, have on us as musicians? Is there still any passion and creativity left, or have we distanced ourselves not only from our fans but from each other? I've been thinking about these questions a lot lately. Especially after what happened in Montreal. Maybe you can help us find answers. Are you up for it?"

"Absolutely! Sounds like an interesting concept. It will be an honour, too."

"OK, great. Let me talk to O'Rourke first. We'll work on the details later. I'll get back to you, soon."

And with that, the phone call was over.

I took another deep breath and smiled. It wasn't such a bad day after all. It looked like I was back in business; in business with Pink Floyd. That was not something I wanted to screw up.

I slowly rose from the couch, poured the remaining whisky in the sink, and made myself a cup of coffee.

29
GOODBYE BLUE SKY

Super Bear Studios, Berre-les-Alpes, France, June 1979

I steered my brand-new Peugeot 305 through the narrow streets of Berre-les-Alpes. It had taken me three days to reach the South of France, and since leaving the motorway a while back, I'd been driving through aromatic Mediterranean hills and vineyards under an azure blue sky. It vindicated my decision not to take the plane. Warm pine and lavender-scented air wafted through the open window. A symphony of crickets and birdsong out-performed the sounds of the car. It was driving heaven.

I felt a surge of excitement run through me in anticipation of the days ahead. I was heading to meet my all-time favourite band. Strictly by invitation only. Bring it on, I thought, all geared up and eager to put fresh ink to paper.

After stopping a few times to check the directions on my huge Michelin map, I finally pulled into the car park of a large white building with an overhanging roof. I got out, stretched, and walked towards the entrance. A sign next to the building said Super Bear Studios.

The front door was locked. I rang the bell. A bloke opened the door, gave me a good once-over.

"Qui?"

"Hi, I'm Matt. I'm here to see Pink Floyd. Roger Waters invited me."

"Wait there, I'll check," he said, and closed the door, leaving me standing outside on the front porch.

After a while, the door opened again, and another guy appeared. He shook my hand and introduced himself.

"Hi, I'm Damon." he said, his accent very French. "Sorry for the wait but we can't have people just walking in when recordings are going on. Please, you can follow me. Roger isn't here yet, but Nick and David are."

I followed Damon through the corridors into one of the recording rooms. Nick Mason was fiddling with some mics he was fitting next to his drum kit. Hearing us come in, he looked up. "Matthias!"

"Monsieur Nick!" I shouted back with a semi-French accent. "Bonjour mon ami, good to see you again!"

He got up from his knees, walked over and gave me a solid hug.

"Roger warned me you were coming. I'm surprised Damon let you in!" he said, feigning surprise.

"I thought he was the new drummer," Damon threw back and walked out of the room.

"Go get yourself a coffee from the kitchen. I'll join you when I've fixed this mess," Nick said, pointing at the mics and cables in front of his kit.

I opted for a glass of cold water instead and sat in the kitchen going through my list of questions and the keywords for topics I wanted to address.

"Let's go out for lunch," Nick suggested, joining me a little while later. "I know an excellent restaurant just down the road."

"Brilliant, I'm starving," I replied.

"So, how are the recordings going?" I asked as soon as we hit the street.

"Slow." Nick said, walking along beside me. "And that may be the understatement of the year."

"It must be hard concentrating on work in these temperatures and with the sun shining. I'd rather work here than rainy old England though, that's for sure."

"Unfortunately, we're not here to escape the British weather," Nick sighed.

"Nor for the great facilities, I'd imagine. Compared to Abbey Road, the studio here is pretty-run-of-the mill, and smaller."

"Yeah, we can't record at home at the moment," Nick said matter-of-factly. "Actually, we can't live at home either for the rest of the year."

His pace suddenly slowed then stopped and fixing me with a penetrating stare said:

"Matt, I'm not sure I want this out there, yet. It's best if you don't write about it right now. In fact, I think it's probably best if you don't let on to the guys we talked about it either. OK?"

"Sure. That's fine. No problem, Nick."

"Good. That's settled. The thing is, we've kind of been exiled," he let out, adding as he started walking again. "We're not allowed back in the country for a year."

"Huh? How come?"

"It's a long and complicated story, but mainly for tax reasons. Let's get a table first and then I'll bring you up to date."

▪ ▪ ▪

We found Nick's restaurant and sat at a table on the pavement outside. A few locals were sitting chatting on a bench under some plane trees on the square opposite us, but apart from that it was pretty quiet. The waiter immediately recognised my host and came over. After ordering some water and wine for us, Nick continued with his story.

"When we were starting out back in the 60s, because of the advances they paid us, any money we got went straight to the record company and we were damn poor. We'd buy our drinks at an off-licence to avoid paying pub prices and drive home rather than stay in a hotel, however far it was. It wasn't like we earned enough money to be ripped off or anything. But we knew plenty of musicians back then who were being fleeced. We were lucky that by the time the money started to come in, we'd already partnered with Peter Jenner and Andrew King. Their management company, Blackhill, made sure we were looked after pretty well."

I wasn't sure where Nick was going with all this but at that point, the waiter arrived with our drinks and the menu. We broke the conversation to order food: a steak sandwich and salad for Nick and a salad niçoise for me. Nick then took up where he'd left off.

"Our last few albums made us a lot of money, I mean serious loads of it. We'd brought in Peter Barnes and set up Pink Floyd Music Publishing by this time, so we were handling it all ourselves. That was six years ago. My share of the royalties from Dark Side Of The Moon bought Lindy and I our big house in Highgate, and it allowed me to indulge in my passion for classic cars. So, we were all doing pretty well for a band that had effectively been looking after itself since the days of Atom Heart Mother."

"You've earned it," I said, and I raised my glass up towards him and took a sip of the nicely chilled white wine. "It's also completely up to you what you spend your money on. You can buy this town and turn it into Disneyland for all I care. But it still doesn't explain why you can't go home."

"There's more to the story," Nick continued, lowering his voice as if the tables on the empty terrace might overhear him, "but, please, remember that this is really all very confidential." I nodded and with a bit of a weary sigh he carried on.

"When the earnings from Dark Side and Wish You Were Here came rolling in, and with the tax rates in the UK being what they are, we were advised to run our money through a financial planning company called Norton Warburg. They would take our gross income and invest it in various businesses so we wouldn't be liable for as much tax. It's a system. They call it venture capital. Anyway, we ended up involved in carbon fibre rowing boats, pizzas, a restaurant on a floating barge, a children's shoe manufacturer and a skateboarding firm called Benji Boards. I kid you not! It was all legal and legitimate, but all the businesses failed miserably. Not only that, Warburg's cronies whizzed the same money between different dodgy accounts and paid themselves huge management fees each time they did it. Without knowing it, we each lost about a million quid. A million quid! It was nearly everything we'd made from Dark Side. Eventually one of our own advisers picked up on the set-up, but it was too late. Norton Warburg were approved by the Bank of England, so we weren't the only ones to get burned. Many people lost their money apart from us."

I stared in disbelieve at the familiar face on the opposite side of the table. Lost all the money they'd made from their records to avoid paying tax? Luckily, the waiter arrived with our food, so I had a few seconds to think of something comforting to say. But before I could come up with anything, Nick carried on.

"It gets worse. It turns out that as we've been investing with pre-tax money - the whole point of the exercise - the Inland Revenue could hit us with an enormous tax bill. And I mean huge. According to our advisors, they could claim as much as 83 percent of the money we lost. That's like somewhere between 5 and 12 million. We can't possibly pay that. It doesn't help that rather than a single venture capital company, we actually have one each. That quadruples our overall tax implications. So basically, we've been told we must live outside the country for at least a year. We left the UK in April. That means we can't go back until April next year. In the meantime, we've got to earn some money and our accountants and tax specialists have to sort the situation out."

"Oh man, that really sucks!" I cried and no longer feeling hungry, I pushed my salad aside and filled our glasses from the bottle the waiter had left on the table. Can't you sue the company, what were they called, Norton Warburg?"

"Nah. Like I said, most of it was all completely legal. We've mostly got ourselves to blame. Besides, somebody told me the owner, Andrew Warburg, has fled the country. All we can do is restructure the way we work and negotiate with Inland Revenue."

"It must be pretty tough on your families, as well..."

"It sure is. Roger is probably going to move to Switzerland, David, and Rick to Greece. I'm not sure where Lindy and I will stay, but I think I'll live here at the studio for a while. It's looking like Rick will stay here, too. And all the while, we're busy working on the new album. That's why Roger and David have temporarily hired villas in the area."

"Must be hard to concentrate on the music with all this going on?"

Nick took a bite from his sandwich.

"Yes, it really is," he glumly admitted. "We're all focussed on getting the new album out, but it's a super challenge because nobody is in the right frame of mind for coming up with fresh ideas. Rog has taken the lead. He played us some demos last July. The quality of the tapes wasn't brilliant, but there was enough there for me to hear the musical potential. David didn't care for it too much. But he and Rick have been working on their own solo projects, and neither of them have put out any of their own ideas as far as the band's concerned. So, we agreed to give one of Roger's ideas a try. We did a couple of rough versions of some tracks at the Britannia Row Studios at the end of last year and Roger's now rewriting the complete piece. We're recording it bit by bit and we've brought Bob Ezrin in to help us on the production side."

"Bob Ezrin? Hasn't he done some work with Lou Reed and Alice Cooper?"

"Yeah, that's right. Carolyne introduced him to us. She used to work for Bob."

"Did he recommend this studio?"

"No. Both Rick and David worked on solo projects here and liked the atmosphere. I mean, what's not to like? It's got its own tennis court, a pool, and plenty of space to hang out in. And it's only a thirty-minute drive from Nice. We had our gear flown over from Britannia Row so we can't complain."

"How's the work going so far?" I asked.

"Like wading through treacle, it's so slow. I've got quite a lot of the drum tracks laid down, but I've got this ominous feeling that getting this album out is going to be a long and complex process."

"Why's that?"

"You should ask Dave and Rick about that. They're not that interested, or that's how it feels. Maybe it's because Roger is pulling all the strings and has involved Ezrin. I don't know. It would be interesting to hear what David has to say about it. I am not sure if you, or anybody, can get through to Rick though. He doesn't seem very happy these days. Maybe it's the money thing or the moving. He's a tough man to read."

"Working in a band can be tough," I conjectured.

"You've got that right! The relationships are very close. And you're not working together out of love particularly, but because of everything that comes out it. It can be murder having to be with people you're not, well, seeing eye to eye with and inevitably there are moments when you feel like packing it all in."

Roger's words on the phone popped into my mind.

"Does anybody want to leave the band?" I asked.

"No, not really," Nick said, looking away. Was he avoiding eye contact, I wondered?

"I think there's a lot of frustration, particularly among the writers, which I'm not. Roger, for example, sometimes has to fight to get his ideas across. Or when Roger is cool, Rick or Dave get frustrated because they're being made to do something they don't like. Garçon!"

Nick waived the waiter over and picked up the check. I thanked him for the lunch and we walked back to the studio together. We didn't talk much, but we both had plenty on our minds.

I spent the rest of the afternoon making small talk with the studio crews and a friendly English engineer called James Guthrie. I also chatted briefly with Dave Gilmour, who agreed to meet me next morning. With that done, I left for the city of Menton where I had booked a hotel. The wine and Nick's intriguing but upsetting stories had taken their toll. After the long day's journey, I longed for a bed and a good night's sleep.

■ ■ ■

I arrived at the studio around 9 a.m. Not your average hour to start recording or interviewing, but I was meeting David at 10. Apart from James Guthrie, who was already busy doing his thing in the control room, the place was deserted. I got myself a coffee, jotted down some notes about the previous day and waited for whatever was to come.

Like clockwork, David arrived at ten and invited me over for coffee in the garden, where we, according to David, could "sit on a bench, talk quietly and enjoy the early morning sun." With a mix of curiosity and some well-hidden animosity, he politely asked about my intentions with the book. It had been Roger's idea after all, and he wanted to know what I was going to write about. I'd been expecting the question and explained that it would be my view on how Pink Floyd works as a band. My own personal perspective. I assured him he had nothing to worry about, and promised that the band would have full editing rights to the manuscript. I wouldn't publish anything without the consent of the band and Steve O'Rourke. Just as I had agreed with Roger a few weeks before I'd left for the trip. I also assured him I was sufficiently informed to know what I could and what I couldn't write. It was all a matter of trust, I said. That seemed to reassure David because he visibly relaxed.

I told David about the lunch with Nick, but I didn't mention the Norton Warburg story.

"Thanks, for having me over," I said. "Can't believe it's already eleven years ago since we first met outside of the Paradiso in Amsterdam."

"Ah, the Paradiso. I remember it well. It took a long time for me to feel part of the band after Syd left. We were such a strange outfit. I found it exceedingly difficult to know what we were doing. People were very down on us after Syd left. They all thought Syd was Pink Floyd's mastermind, and they basically dismissed the rest of us. Even our management company, Blackhill, believed in Syd more than the band. We really didn't start coming back until Saucerful Of Secrets and the first free concert in Hyde Park."

"Syd's like a ghost who comes back to haunt you now and then. People keep referring to him even to this day," I stated.

"I'm used to it by now. I've never forgotten when the band was recording See Emily Play, and Syd asked me to come along to the studio. He completely blanked me when I got there. And there was this one terrible night when Syd came to the Middle Earth club in Covent Garden and stood in front of the stage staring at me all night long. It was horrible! He really is one of rock 'n' roll's great tragedies. He was one of the most talented people I've ever met and a brilliant songwriter. If he'd not gone haywire, he could have beaten a guy like Ray Davies hands down."

Moving on, I asked what he thought about Roger's new demos. And how much money Roger had offered him to go along with his ideas. I expected him to smile. Instead, David's reaction, although still softly spoken, was stern and agitated.

"Roger gave us all a cassette of the whole thing, and I just couldn't listen to it. It was too depressing and boring. We eventually agreed to do it, but we had to throw out a lot of stuff, rewrite some bits and add in a lot of new material. I like the basic idea and we all think the concept is strong. But for me, a lot of it is irrelevant. I don't feel the pressure of a wall between me and my audience."

"A wall?"

"It's the central theme of the album. It was sparked by an incident in Montreal when Roger spat a fan full in the face."

"I remember him telling me about it. It wasn't something he was particularly proud of."

"I don't feel the things that happen, some of which have also not been so wonderful, impact on my life to the same degree Roger feels them affect his life. Like never having known his father, for example. That's his viewpoint, and he's perfectly entitled to it. But I don't subscribe to it. I feel an affinity with Dark Side Of The Moon and Wish You Were Here and I can see the truth in Animals, although I probably don't paint people as black as that. This stuff we're working on now is all a bit, well, glum. And I'm not a glum person. Roger's writing is predominantly introspective."

"Is that a problem?" I asked.

"Well, if you're only looking at the worst aspects of the world, reflecting on them exclusively, it can be."

David just about managed to produce a faint smile as I ploughed on.

"He has obviously taken the lead on this album. How does that work in the studio?"

"Roger is one of the main producers. Not only because it's his idea, but he is also exceptionally good with the production side of things. As far as Pink Floyd's records are concerned, I've co-produced all of them. While I might not argue with Roger much over lyrics, I think I know as much as anyone about music and, sure, I make my opinions known. Bob Ezrin helps smooth issues between Roger and me, I guess. If we were just left to get on with it, we'd probably just sit around bickering all day. Someone would say, 'I don't like that one very much,' someone else might agree, and then Roger would look all sulky and come in the next day with something brilliant. He's been great at that these last days. Especially now it's his brainchild we're working on."

"He's not just showing off?"

"We've always wanted to be a rock band, meet girls, get rich and have fun. And yes, if I'm honest about it, maybe our overarching motive is to show off. Although it is a rather pleasant side-effect, our driving force isn't money. All rock stars desperately need to show off, you know. It's because we've all got these weak egos."

"I always thought the two of you got along pretty well. Not the best of friends, but brothers-in-arms, so to speak. Correct?"

"Roger and I have a good working relationship. We argue a lot, mind you, and sometimes heatedly, but it's mostly artistic disagreements like who takes lead vocals and stuff. I'm glad we're still achieving things that are valid."

"Are you and Roger able to compromise to meet each other?"

"That's a good question. I don't look on compromise as a dirty word. In Pink Floyd we argue, fight and come to a compromise on things. Sometimes that leads to bad feelings, but they only last for a day or two. I really think we work well together. I can remember fantastic moments during the making of Wish You Were Here when we were really, really close. Moments like that still exist. It's just that these days we have to work harder to make the magic happen."

"What about Rick? How does he fit in the big picture?"

"To be honest, I'm not really sure. He hasn't really been doing a lot of late. But I don't want to get into that now."

It was as if David had sensed Roger's approach because, suddenly, there he was standing next to us.

"Don't believe a fuckin' word he's saying," Roger joked and turning to his band mate said. "You're wanted in the studio, Dave."

David Gilmour rose from the bench. "Thanks for the chat, Matt. See you in a bit."

Roger Waters was about to follow David back to the main building, but after a couple of steps, he turned and said: "Bob and I want to check out another studio tomorrow. It's an hour's drive from here. Care to join the party?"

"Sure, sounds like fun."

"I'll pick you up at eleven then. If we play our cards right, we might even borrow Nicky's Daytona."

"Cool! As long as you let me do the driving," I said smiling.

"Don't push it, Matt. Wrecking Ferrari's is for professionals only," Roger quipped and left.

The rest of the day was pretty uneventful. The band and the studio technicians were hard at work recording and tweaking a few fragmented bits and pieces.

▪ ▪ ▪

The next day made up for the humdrum of the day before. I mentioned over an early coffee with James Guthrie that I couldn't recognise any melody or structure in the fragments yet. He took me to the control room and played a couple of the work-in-progress songs. The intense dynamics of the music surprised me. These were all basic tracks with little detail or added effects, but the tunes were there and what I heard was dramatic, sharp-edged and it had an overall harsh roughness to it. It was unlike anything I'd heard from Pink Floyd before, and I could understand why David had called it a 'bit glum'. Glum or not, I knew I was listening to the start of something special.

Guthrie told me the album was going to be called The Wall and that Roger already had the whole concept mapped out with most of the lyrics and song titles in place. He also let slip that "there was a lot at stake" for the band and that he sincerely hoped this "monster of a project" would make the tight deadlines.

Roger arrived to pick me up, dangled the keys to a Ferrari in front of my face.

"Hope you brought a pair of clean undies to France, Matt. You're going to need them."

"Hope you've paid your insurance bills," I retorted.

"As long as Nick has, we're OK!"

Roger explained that as Bob was driving to the Miraval studios straight from his hotel in Nice, we could use the mean-looking red Daytona two-seater. With strict instructions from its owner, of course. The first part of our journey took us to a place called Correns. Even if he'd wanted to, navigating the maze of narrow bendy roads meant it was virtually impossible to exceed the speed limit.

Seizing the opportunity to pose some questions, I asked Roger where the idea for The Wall had come from.

"That's a good question," he said, keeping his eyes firmly on the small roads ahead. "I started to work on my own more not long after the release of Animals. I'd escaped to the country by then and drafted a couple of concepts that were rattling around my head. One I called The Pros And Cons Of Hitch-Hiking and the other Bricks In The Wall. I presented the pieces to the band back at Britannia Row and told them I wanted one to be a solo album and the other the next Pink Floyd release. Except for Steve O'Rourke, who preferred The Pros And Cons, they all chose The Wall as concept for the band's new album."

"You remember the spitting incident I told you about?" Roger continued. "It made me seriously question my life and what I was doing. Things had been going wrong ever since we blew up in such a gigantic way. I'd begun to feel alienated and alone, especially playing in huge stadiums where it felt like nobody took us seriously. I felt the loss of the intimacy of the ordinary relationship between musicians and their audience. To protect myself, I built a wall and shut myself off behind it. Walls can sometimes be good things. Isolating yourself from the world is not. It's legit to feel pain deeply in ways that change your life. Shut yourself off, and you bring about your own destruction. That's what the new album will be about."

"How about the rest of the band? Do they go along with your views and ideas?"

"That's a thing, sure. There's nobody in the band I can talk to about any of this stuff. Dave's just not interested, and Rick has become pretty closed recently. Nick would be happy to listen because we've always been good mates, but he's more interested in his racing cars these days. No, what I needed was a collaborator, someone I could talk to. That's why we took on Bob Ezrin. He's musically and intellectually in a place more similar to where I am."

"It must be frustrating, not being able to share ideas..."

"It can be sometimes. We were a cracking team when we were younger, from, say, 1968 until Dark Side. We were a tight-knit group and we've achieved everything we set out to achieve together. But these days, well, I've believe our soul motives for staying together are fear and greed."

"That's quite a grim and dark take on the band, Roger."

"Well, to you it might look that these recordings are a group collaboration. Well, OK, the others collaborate on it, but they are not collaborators, if you know what I mean. It is in no sense a democratic process. If somebody has a good idea, I'll accept it and maybe use it, or maybe not. Like a director who's directing a movie will take onboard things the actors have to say. The Wall will be a terrific piece of work and I'm already proud of it."

"Still, you can't make it alone," I protested. "Whichever way you look at it, it's still be a band effort."

"Not quite. It's all a matter of perspective. Rick has put in almost nothing so far; we still have to record the keyboard parts. Nick plays the drums, but with a little help from some friends. And Dave? Dave plays the guitar and has written the music for a few songs, but he contributes nothing else, really. The collaboration with Ezrin is a fertile one. But there's only one chief, and that's me."

“Why are we checking out another studio, anyway?”

“I find singing at a higher altitude quite a challenge. It somehow affects my vocal cords. That’s one reason. The other one is that I prefer solitude when I’m laying down the vocal tracks. I don’t want to have to explain myself or defend whether I use an idea. I don’t want any distractions. I want to do this right.”

We hit the A8 motorway and Roger floored the pedal. The engine roared, and I fell silent.

29
MAROONED

Calling from home, November 1979

The country code of the number scribbled on the pad in front of me was for Greece, not Los Angeles, where I knew Pink Floyd was putting the finishing touches to The Wall. They had ousted Rick Wright from the band. I was about to call him and was not looking forward to the conversation.

Reportedly, it was Roger who had set the wheels in motion. He thought Rick wasn't pulling his weight and was unhappy he only showed up for the keyboard tracks. According to Roger, Rick didn't contribute on the production side of things and Roger got so hacked off he refused to give Rick credits. It's the first time a Pink Floyd album will not name all four Pink Floyd members in the production credits and it didn't go down too well with Rick, obviously, who will lose out on royalties when the record is released.

But it wasn't only that. The band had agreed to deliver the new album at the beginning of October and planned their holidays in August accordingly. While they were away, Roger realised they were running short on time and asked Bob Ezrin to get Rick over to Los Angeles so they could put the keyboard parts down a week earlier. Rick had refused point blank, and through Steve O'Rourke who phoned in the news, told Roger "to fuck off". Roger was furious. He already felt burdened with more than his share of the work, and it outraged him Rick made no effort to help. That regardless of the circumstances, Rick was unprepared to break off his holiday, was the straw that broke the camel's back. O'Rourke gave Rick an ultimatum: either he'd agree to finish the album, keep all the royalties due to him, but leave quietly when it was all over, or there would be a long battle and no album. Worried about the financial consequences of not releasing the album, Rick agreed to go back to work.

Fortunately, the press had not yet picked up the news. I had to find out for myself how much of all this was true. Thankful I'd asked Rick for his phone number shortly before I left France, I noticed my hand trembling as I dialled the number.

"Hello?"

"Richard?" I always address him as Richard rather than Rick. No idea why.

"Yes, who's this?"

"It's Matt. Mind having a little chat? I've heard some disturbing news and wondered how you were doing..."

"I'm fine, Matt. Thanks. I'm pretty pissed off, though."

"Pink Floyd..."

"It's a bloody tombstone round my neck."

I told Rick what I'd heard so far.

"I'm curious to hear your side of the story."

"Well, as you'll have noticed during your visit to France, James Guthrie usually worked with Roger and David during the day and returned at night to record with me. Like we agreed upon in the past, I expected everybody to get a producer's credit on the album, but Bob Ezrin wasn't happy with my contribution. It's true that I was feeling under a lot of pressure and things between me and Juliette were not going well, mainly because I wasn't spending much time at home. The rest of the band's kids are young enough to stay with them in France, but mine are older and must go to school. I hadn't seen them for months and missed them terribly. I just couldn't bring myself to cut our family holiday short. I desperately needed the quality time."

"Creatively there were no differences?" I asked, weighing my words carefully.

"Not directly, although there were a couple of times when I thought 'Oh no, here we go again: it's all about the war, about his mother, about losing his father...' I hoped he'd work through all of that, but for Roger it's a fixation. He writes in the same tempo, the same key, same everything. If it wasn't for the financial situation, we might have piped up and said we didn't much like the songs and done something different. But Roger had the material, Dave and I didn't."

"The real tombstone is not so much the band; it's the pressure of making money."

"In theory, we're bankrupt. Our accountants have lost all our money and we owe huge amounts of tax. We need to finish the album in time so we can pay it all back. So yes, it is a scary time for us all."

"And now the band has fired you?"

"Believe me, I wanted to work, but Roger was making it exceedingly difficult for me. I think he wanted me out from the start."

"Why would he want that?"

"Roger and I were never the best of friends, but we weren't enemies either. He's on some sort of huge ego trip. It's like he wants to control everything. I think he has this big leadership game plan in which he does all the writing and producing, and a bunch of musicians play whatever he tells them to. They may be buddies, but I think he's set on getting rid of Nick too. That's what I've heard, anyway. He and Dave don't want a band, they want to use session musicians. You can believe it or not, what you like, but I suspect that's how he's thinking."

"How did you find out you were no longer welcome?"

"After we finished recording in France, we all took a break and I went to see my family in Greece. One day, I got a call from Steve saying 'Come to LA immediately, Roger wants you to start recording keyboard tracks.' I explained that I hadn't seen my kids for months and couldn't leave them, but that I'd be there on the agreed date.' He said: 'Fair enough, I understand.' Not long after, he told me that Roger wanted me out of the band."

"Man, that sucks... Why didn't you fight his decision?"

"I tried! Dave and Nick both backed me up and said they thought it wasn't right and that Roger was being unfair. But when we had a meeting, Roger said 'Look, either you leave, or I'll not let you record my material for The Wall.' Maybe he was bluffing, but that's what he said. You know the terrible financial mess we're in, well then he said: 'You can get your full royalties for the album, but you leave now, and we'll get a keyboard player to finish it.' I spent days and a lot of sleepless nights thinking about the whole thing."

"You could have called his bluff..."

"Well, I thought about it, but I can't work with the guy anymore. The money situation is terrifying and if you ask me, the whole band is falling apart. I don't know what would have happened if I'd said 'No, I'll not go.' So, rightly or wrongly, I left. I'll finish recording this album and I'll do the live shows following the release and then we'll say goodbye."

There was an uncomfortable pause.

"How do you feel now?" It was all I could think of asking.

"Angry. This is my band as much as it's his. I feel it's wrong. Sure, I wasn't particularly happy with the band, the way it was going. I'm not trying to put him down and I think he has great ideas, but Roger is a difficult man to work with.

Whatever I tried to do; he would say it was wrong. It was impossible for me to work with him, really. Hopefully, one day he'll admit that what he did was unfair. So you could say I'm angry, yeah."

"What happens now?"

"I want to carry on playing live. I'm quite prepared to swallow my pride and go out there and play with them for a wage. Nobody needs to know I'm not actually one of the band members anymore. I'm just going to accept what has happened and make the best of it. Not sure what I will do after the tour, but I'm sure as hell it won't involve working with Pink Floyd."

38

WELCOME TO THE MACHINE

Regency Café & Wembley Stadium, London, August 6, 1988

The shit had hit the proverbial fan.

I was sitting in a café with the leftovers from breakfast, a pile of recent media clippings and an official-looking letter in front of me. The press releases weren't pretty, but the letter I'd received by fax earlier this morning had me seriously worried. I swore silently into my cappuccino and picked it up.

The official company letterhead was from Peter Rudge and was written by some staff employee on behalf of Roger Waters. Rudge was a significant player in music management and looked after rock icons like The Stones, The Who, Lynyrd Skynyrd, Duran Duran and Madness. He had recently taken Roger under his wing. The letter demanded that I immediately cease and desist from working on the book, claiming, correctly, that the work was long overdue, that it was Roger Waters' initiative anyway, and that because of a change in circumstances, to publish a book about Waters and Pink Floyd at this present moment would do more harm than good. They didn't ask me to reply, but the tone of the letter made quite clear that opposing the 'request' would not be a good idea.

I felt slightly intimidated and maybe a bit hurt. Why had Roger not bothered to call or write me himself? It's not as if I wouldn't have gone along with him. He's a tough person to say 'no' to, and I'm sure he could have bent me to his will. I thought we were friends. He could have just asked me nicely.

The timing didn't surprise me, though. Things were not good in the Floyd universe. The antagonism between Roger and David had gone way beyond a war of words and was now a full-blown legal battle. Somewhere last year, Gilmour and Mason had brought Rick Wright back in as a hired hand and together they'd released A Momentary Lapse Of Reason under the Floyd moniker. Roger was livid, and, in a pre-emptive push back, brought forward the release of Radio K.A.O.S., his second solo-album. Unfortunately, Pink Floyd's publicity machine far surpassed that of Roger on a global scale and the angry bass player's move backfired, as the follow-up tours of the two camps soon painfully made clear. Whereas Roger and his Bleeding Heart Band (with Paul Carrack and Andy Fairweather-Low, amongst others) were booked for a measly forty gigs and had trouble even selling out those, Pink Floyd was playing to packed venues and stadiums all over the world. They were still touring now and would be until well into 1989. It just so happened I was going to see them play at Wembley Stadium for the second time in a row, tonight. Tickets for all the concerts had sold out months in advance. Pink Floyd's brand magic was as potent as ever. A world full of loyal fans was out there gunning for them. Roger Waters no longer had that luxury to fall back on.

▪ ▪ ▪

I liked the Regency Café and its art deco interior with yellow brick tiles, formica tables and some good local food on the menu. It was like stepping forty years back in time. It was also within walking distance of the hotel where I was staying. I ordered myself another coffee, put down the nasty bit of paper and turned my attention to the pile of press clippings. I'd already read most of them, but as I like to understand these issues before forming my own thoughts and views, I'd went through them again.

"Roger is a dog in the manger and I'm going to fight him," read the article from a 1985 Sunday Times that was on top of the pile.

David Gilmour wasn't beating about the bush, I thought, although I was unconvinced he would have used those exact words. It didn't really sound like the mellow and cautious person I knew.

The piece was about the bitter legal battles surrounding Roger Waters' departure from Pink Floyd; how he'd proclaimed the musical partnership a "spent force", resigned, and then tried to block anyone from using the Pink Floyd name ever again. He'd even taken it as far as the High Courts. When it turned out the partnership had never been formalised and there was nothing to block, Gilmour and Mason upheld their conviction that they had the legal right to continue as Pink Floyd and, in between responding to Waters' escalating suits, did so, regardless.

Getting to the root of all the evil was difficult and complicated. I knew from first-hand experience that David and Roger were not the best of friends. They never had been, their two personalities were just too far apart for that. In the beginning, each on a quest for fame and fortune, they were willing to put most differences aside. But after the money train came rolling in, their relationship completely disintegrated. Roger had already intimated there were problems that day I spent with him at the Sunningdale Golf

Club. I read little into it at the time. It's not as if you have to be best friends to release brilliant records. It was only when I got to France, that I understood how much tension there really was. I knew that something or somebody had to give.

I moved on to a last year's "inside story" by Rolling Stone's David Fricke. In it, he explained the acrimony worsened when Roger moved to take creative control and forced his way to become the central figure. "That was not the best thing to happen," Gilmour told Fricke. "Pink Floyd could have made better records if Roger had been willing to back off a little and be more open to other people's input." The whole thing came to a head during the recording of The Final Cut, when Gilmour, who disliked the album and felt Waters had forced it on them, publicly criticised some songs as being offcuts from The Wall and "not up to snuff". Roger had offered to do it as a solo recording and pay the others for the costs they'd made. Good or bad, the album was a guaranteed paycheck, and as Roger told Fricke: "... they know songs don't grow on trees. They wanted it to be a Floyd record."

In the end, they released The Final Cut in 1983 as a Pink Floyd effort and sold three million copies. Not a huge number for Pink Floyd. Any illusion that the trio would ever work together again was shattered. Roger wanted nothing to do with David and David refused to be a hired hand in a Waters-led Pink Floyd. Nick, caught unhappily in the middle of the hostilities, felt that Roger had picked on David unfairly throughout the Final Cut recordings and sided with David. The Floyd to all intents and purposes had died.

▪ ▪ ▪

Cupping my chin in my hands, I contemplated the goings on in Regent Street outside the window. I'd read somewhere about David disliking Roger's attacks on Margaret Thatcher, and that he thought the album was too personal and too political, but what a shambles. The waitress arrived, I took a sip of the bitter caffeinated drink and read on.

After work on The Final Cut was over, the band made no effort to promote the record or take it on tour. No plans were made for the future. Instead, they went their separate ways and worked on individual projects. David recorded and toured his About Face album, Roger did the same with The Pros And Cons Of Hitch Hiking, and, a year later, Nick released Profiles, his second solo effort.

As far as Roger was concerned, Pink Floyd was finished and at the end of 1985 he admitted as much to the press. Gilmour, though, was reluctant to see the Floyd fade into history. In 1986, he and Mason began work on a new album. When Steve O'Rourke tried to pressure Waters into joining them, citing the band's contractual obligations and resultant royalty penalties if they failed to provide new material, Waters fired him and yet another ugly mess was set in motion.

So, it wasn't the Pink Floyd name game that had caused the dissolution, I mused, but a tangentially related business matter. Things weren't getting any prettier, but they were starting to make sense. I drained my now cold coffee.

Although Waters claimed adamantly that it was quite within his rights to fire O'Rourke - how could there be future Pink Floyd records if there was no group? - and that he had given him six months' notice. O'Rourke fought back, claiming just as adamantly his dismissal was illegal. Waters, assuming they could never continue as Pink Floyd without him, offered to relinquish his rights and allowed Mason and Gilmour to continue using the Pink Floyd name if they released him from his recording and publishing obligations and ratify his dismissal of O'Rourke. The offer was rejected.

By the summer of '86, Waters was faced with lawsuits over the management deal and lost royalties. In a boardroom meeting he told the band: "... if those papers come through my door, we all go to court. I am not going to be hung out to dry in court for years and years while you guys are calling yourselves Pink Floyd." In October, he sued Gilmour and Mason to prevent them from using the name Pink Floyd.

For David Gilmour, the situation was intolerable. He may not have been a Pink Floyd founding member, but he'd invested an awful lot of time in the band and had no intention of giving up. As he told Fricke: "I was damned if I was going to be forced out. I am an extremely stubborn person, and they will not force me out of something I consider to be partly mine. We never sat down at any point during the recording of A Momentary Lapse Of Reason and said, 'It doesn't sound Floyd enough. Make this more Floyd.' We just worked on the songs until they sounded right. When they sounded great and right, that's when it became Pink Floyd."

Roger dismissed David's assertion out of hand, saying of the album: "I think it's a very facile but quite clever forgery. If you don't listen to it too closely, it does sound like Pink Floyd. It's got Dave Gilmour playing guitar. And with the considered intention of setting out to make something that sounds like everyone's conception of a Pink Floyd record, it's inevitable that you achieve that limited goal. I think the songs are poor in general. The lyrics I can't believe. I'm sure it will do very well."

I put the page aside and sighed. Things would only get more complicated, I knew.

During the recording of A Momentary Lapse Of Reason, both sides kept each other distracted with endless phone calls and meetings with lawyers. By this time, Pink Floyd had brought Bob Ezrin back in as co-producer. Roger was also considering Ezrin as producer for his Radio K.A.O.S. album, which only added fuel to the already blazing fire. Ezrin later blamed an over-stretched schedule and family pressures for preventing him from working on Roger's record. Roger, not amused, retaliated mercilessly.

I picked up yet another article, this time from Q Magazine. In it, David recalls recording with the band in Los Angeles in '87. While trying to get the tour dates fixed, every single promoter in North America was bombarded with letters from Roger threatening to sue them and seal their bank accounts. According to David, Pink Floyd had "a team of lawyers in every city ready and briefed in case it was suddenly in front of a judge and we had to get someone there in 20 minutes." It never happened, but the band had to be prepared for it and the whole business "cost them an awful lot of money."

I remembered reading that there were some attempts at reconciliation. I went through the pile of clippings and found the story I was looking for. The article, published in Creem Magazine, described that they had made some efforts to get Nick and Roger together over a dinner table. As neither party really understood the legal implications of all the goings on, later discussions had come to nothing. Never in the entire career of the band had anybody ever put anything on paper about how to deal with situations like these. Roger needed the band to be disbanded to clear the way for his solo career, and he just assumed it would happen. No one expected that out of David's stubbornness would come a new Floyd album, let alone Roger.

They finally settled at the end of last year. After two years of bickering, all parties took a break from touring and met on David's houseboat, The Astoria, to finalise an agreement that freed Roger from his contractual agreements with Steve O'Rourke, allowed him to keep control of The Wall and gave David and Nick the legal right to continue working as Pink Floyd.

After the divorce papers were signed and the dust had settled, it was time for some reflection. A sensible Nick Mason was quoted in Creem magazine saying: "We lost a major contributor when Roger left, but it's galvanised us to do things that we would never have done if Roger had stayed. Dave would never have applied himself to writing. Well, I won't say never, he might have, over the period of the next seven to ten years. Speaking as the observer, I think Dave has not so much trouble with music. In fact, it comes very naturally to him, but the lyrics were pretty much murder. He did a sort of crash course in writing lyrics and, by the end of the album, they were really sort of flying out."

I loved how Nick could put things into perspective with some intelligent remarks and a touch of wit. I continued reading the Creem article: "From David's point of view, I think he got an enormous benefit from Roger leaving. From my point of view there is another enormous benefit, just from the sheer pleasure of getting on with it, enjoying the work and playing live. Dave and I were always the ones who liked the idea of going out and play. Roger didn't. He's touring now and probably finds it a lot easier with him having total control. But he still doesn't have that genuine enthusiasm for playing onstage."

And now Roger wants me to quit working on the book. Not such a big deal, given the circumstances. I didn't want to interfere or poke around in any still open wounds between him and Pink Floyd. Nor did I relish having to choose sides. I'd lost my interest in writing after the release of The Final

Cut, anyway. I was too busy running a family. Anna and I got married three years ago and we now had a little baby girl to care about. We'd called her Elisa. Elisa had completely changed my perspective on the world and about the things that really matter in life. Raising a baby and the responsibilities that come along with it had made me a milder, more forgiving person. It took a while to accept the years of daydreaming were over, but all I cared about now was being a good dad to little miss sunshine and giving her a bright future to look forward to. The book could definitely wait.

I wondered what the future had in store for the Waters-less Floyd. Would a reconciliation ever be possible? Never in a million years, I thought, putting the bits of paper back into my bag.

I paid the bill at the counter and walked out into the Saturday sun. I was looking forward to a day of browsing and shopping in my favourite record stores, and made my way over to Oxford Street. Even though I loved all the small, independent, and second-hand shops of Soho and Camden, I could easily spend a couple of hours in Virgin's Megastore alone. Also on the list was HMV, which had opened two years ago in the attendance of Bob Geldof and Michael Hutchence. I'd never been to the HMV flagship stores before, but it turned out to be a huge and impressive multi-level music lover's paradise. I spend the rest of the afternoon checking out the endless rows of LP's, CD's, books and videos. Eventually, my feet started to protest. With new Living Colour and Frank Zappa releases in the bag, it was time to head back to the hotel for a quick rest.

▪ ▪ ▪

On the tube to Wembley, my thoughts went back to last night. I'd witnessed a new chapter in Pink Floyd's history: the band's first tour without Roger Waters. Apart from David, Nick and Rick, reportedly back on a salary of 11.000 dollars a day, the band now also featured bass player Guy Pratt, percussionist Gary Wallis, Tim Renwick on guitars, keyboard wizard Jon Carin, sax player Scott Page and a group of singers including Durga McBroom who's vocals on Great Gig In The Sky were absolutely spot on. Pink Floyd kicked off the show with a beautiful rendition of Shine On You Crazy Diamond Parts 1-5, followed by a bunch of new songs, including Signs Of Life and Learning To Fly. Both got a lot of airplay recently.

After the break, the band had played Sorrow, The Dogs Of War, One Of These Days, Time, The Great Gig In The Sky, Wish You Were Here, Welcome To The Machine, Us And Them, Money, another Brick In The Wall, Part 2 and Comfortably Numb, with One Slip and Run Like Hell as the closing encores.

It was a good, but not very surprising mixture of old and new songs, but the quadrophonic sound was the best I'd ever heard at any stadium gig. As expected, they'd made a real effort on the props and light show. The giant circular film screen with vintage video footage was back, as was the mirror ball during Comfortably Numb. The inflatable pig was a familiar sight as well, although its testicles were not. We got a flying and exploding bed instead of a plane, and some very cool lasers accompanied Run Like Hell. One 'special effect' wasn't noticeable on stage; I spotted some kids wearing t-shirts 'Who the fuck is Roger Waters?' emblazoned on the front. That made me feel rather sad.

Nobody onstage mentioned the former bass player. In fact, there wasn't much interaction between the band and the audience at all. The performance seemed flawless, perhaps a bit too flawless. It was all rather sterile and calculated. David's guitar playing and vocals were top notch, as were Rick's fluent keyboard sounds, but surrounded by thousands of fans, the impressive multi-media extravaganza didn't affect me as it used to do. I was pleasantly entertained, not musically touched.

An hour later, I was back on Wembley Stadium's pitch for the second day in a row. The gig turned out to be identical to the one the day before and this time, disappointment got the better of me. Why not take a risk on changing at least a couple of songs? I wondered how many people were thinking the same. I was glad I'd paid for both my tickets. No passes and no backstage adventures meant no awkward conversations with the band afterwards. How could I honestly tell them what I thought of their two identical shows without hurting any feelings? And who cared about what I had to say, anyway? According to the enthusiastic roaring and applauding Wembley crowd, Pink Floyd was back to its usual brilliant form. Who was I to think differently? Who was I to say that I missed the intimacy, spontaneity, and urgency of the early days? It wasn't because they were missing a former teammate. Instead, Pink Floyd's live format had affirmed an old, self-fulfilling prophecy: Welcome to the machine.

40

THE POST WAR DREAM

Potsdamer Platz, Berlin, July 21, 1990

I've considered Peter Spottington as one of my closest friends for well over a decade now. He's known to everyone as Sport, which is rather hilarious considering he's more of a book, movie, jazz and the occasional glass of smokey whisky type. Sport hates sport. Years back, Peter confessed he's a huge fan of Sammy Davis Jr, whose portrayal of Sportin' Life, the drug-dealing character in George Gershwin's opera Porgy and Bess, had so impressed him. It was only me who called him Sportin' Life at first, but then it morphed into Sport and everyone started to call him that, even his mother.

Sport and I spent many drinking nights together, and we developed quite a routine. We'd try out a newly discovered brand of whisky, play a board game or two, and we'd introduce each other to new music. This all led to much heated debate and lots of laughter. We seldom seemed to agree on matters of musical taste, but when we did, it was always celebrated in good single malt fashion.

I was the first to introduce Sport to the compact disc in 1984 and we quickly agreed on the new format's superior sound quality. Enter more heated discussions about re-releases of albums we'd both listened to many times before. Sport loathed any musician who sold more than a couple of hundred LP's, or CD's. He was highly suspicious of anything remotely commercial and considered listening to chart music as plain torture. I was determined to convert him to the world of Pink Floyd. Not that I'd not tried before, but with my recently installed shiny new CD player and four magnificent speakers, I was ready to blow him away. I failed. Again.

"A bunch of pretentious slugs," he'd called them. According to Sport, listening to Pink Floyd was like "watching paint dry". Bastard!

Nevertheless, I persuaded the sorry old sod to join me for a long weekend in Berlin. We'd all watched its Wall come down live on tv recently. We both felt, if we wanted to explore the city before McDonald's ruined its streets forever, we shouldn't wait too long. I then came up with a cunning plan of bribery and deceit which involved me offering to pay for the two hotel rooms if Sport would accompany me to the recently announced live rendition of Roger Waters' The Wall. The show was to be performed on a piece of former no-man's-land right in the middle of Berlin's city centre. I even offered to throw in the tickets, as well. At first, Sport protested saying that "Berlin wants nothing to do with megalomaniac ego's anymore," but he proved himself worthy of his name and was a good Sport. Mentioning that Joni Mitchell and Van Morrison were also on the bill, had finally sealed the deal.

▪ ▪ ▪

And here we were, right in the middle of historic Berlin. It felt eerie, almost unreal. Hard to believe that just nine months ago there would have been mines and sentry posts where we were standing and probably a few snipers too, all making sure we couldn't get out of here alive. They were still clearing the land now, in fact, and only two weeks ago the military had found more weapons, ammunition and an old Nazi bunker. The strip of dirt between Potsdamer Platz and the Brandenburg Gate that had divided East from West Berlin for 28 odd years was now nothing more than a long bare stretch of soil and grass. The remains were clearly visible and, for a large part, the Berlin Wall was still standing, only now it was guarding a part of the concert area from unwanted guests.

"This morning I saw some local peddlers selling chunks of concrete to tourists claiming they were pieces of the Wall," Sport said. "Would you believe it? Commerce is rapidly taking over Communism and they're fooling us all."

"I wonder how many of the 300.000 expected today are unaware of the historical context of this place," I asked.

"A multimedia event broadcasted worldwide to commemorate the fall of the Wall? Probably not a lot," Sport answered. "You'd have to be living under a rock not to know the significance. I'm just hoping something good comes out of it all."

"I think something will. Roger plans to donate all profits from the show to a UK charity founded by a veteran wartime pilot."

"Not sure I see the connection with Berlin there..."

"Not with Berlin, no. But I suspect Roger sees the city as the perfect setting for the WOII theme that connects the Wall to his dad. Anyway, I glad he did. This is a pretty amazing place to be right now."

With the TV footage and newspaper images of Germany's reunion still fresh in my mind, I felt privileged to be here, as I suspected Sport did too. Arriving yesterday, we'd used the opportunity to do some sightseeing and had seen enough to be impressed by the obvious difference in wealth between the East and West. Checkpoint Charlie had permanently opened its gates and as you could cross from the one Berlin to the other without a visa, we duly did.

We found the city on the East side to be quiet, drab and old-looking. The few cars we saw were all Trabants, the former GDR's infamous smoke-spewing, motor sputtering vehicle. It was as if the clocks had turned back thirty or forty years. By contrast, the West was noisy, colourful and buzzing with life. The streets were lined with luxury shops, restaurants and clubs and near jammed with prosperous looking cars of every make. The difference couldn't have been bigger. There seemed to be only one thing both sides had in common and that was their smiles. Literally everybody was smiling. A few people admitted to feeling a bit apprehensive about living together with the old adversary, but everyone seemed to be happy and excited about the bright future ahead.

My sense of anticipation was growing, too. Not so much because we were standing at the crossroads of a new Berlin, though. I was about to see Roger Waters perform The Wall and I was overjoyed at the prospect. Considerably more than my travelling companion at any rate. Along with his regular house band, Waters had brought along a veritable army of guest stars including The Band's Rick Danko, Levon Helm and Garth Hudson, The Hooters, Van Morrison, Sinéad O'Connor, Cyndi Lauper, Marianne Faithfull, Scorpions, Joni Mitchell, Paul Carrack, Thomas Dolby and Bryan Adams, along with actors Albert Finney, Jerry Hall, Tim Curry and Ute Lemper.

■ ■ ■

A few months ago, Roger had told me over the phone from his house in Richmond that he was trying to get guest musicians like Peter Gabriel, Bruce Springsteen, Rod Stewart, and Eric Clapton to join him. Apparently, some had been unavailable while others had snubbed the event. Unfortunately, none of his former bandmates were involved either. That really would have been something! A British impresario called Tony Hollingsworth produced the event, with Mark Fisher and Jonathan Park designing the 185 yards long and 27 yards high wall. Even in daylight, with two more hours before showtime, the partly erected wall was already an impressive sight.

Roger, bless his heart, did as he'd promised and sent two passes which I'd received via the record company. The passes granted access to a grandstand and to a huge, tented area where we could sit, eat, and drink amongst other invited guests. At first, I felt a bit put out they had not invited me to meet and greet the artists backstage. But once we arrived in the immense area and saw the unparalleled logistics, distances and attendances involved, I realised we were better off staying put and absorbing the spectacle from the grandstand. I never got the chance to see Pink Floyd's original production of The Wall when they performed in the US, England, and Germany ten years ago, so I was hugely looking forward to it. Some of my excitement was rubbing off on Sport, too, I noticed. He'd stopped making his usual cynical remarks.

"Whatever happed to Pink Floyd's original singer?" Sport asked out of the blue.

"Syd Barrett?"

"Yeah, Syd. I remember listening to one of his solo albums once. Intriguing stuff."

"A deeply sensitive, open and supremely talented guy who kind of lost it, basically. Spends his days at home in Cambridge. Painting. Don't think he has any contact with the outside world or his former bandmates. I've actually met him once...”

“You did?” Sport asked in disbelief.

“In the late sixties. On a ferry from Ibiza to Formentera, my first summer holiday abroad. A friendly, gentle soul. It was almost impossible not to like him. I only really spoke to him once and very briefly, but even then he came over as being emotionally fragile. Syd was only around for one Pink Floyd record, but he was instrumental in getting Pink Floyd started up. I get the impression the band still feels guilty about the way they dealt with the situation. That they couldn’t help him.”

“No hope of him returning to music?”

“Don’t think so. People still mystify the situation. I think that’s absurd. It’s obvious that he can’t and doesn’t want to return to public life, let alone to the limelight of the music industry.”

“Has The Wall anything to do with Syd Barrett?”

“That’s a tough one. The principal theme is about how we build walls around ourselves. It was sparked by an incident in the seventies when Roger Waters spat at a fan who kept trying to climb onto the stage. Roger told me he felt very alienated from his audience. There are also lots of allusions to Roger’s childhood experiences in there. He lost his father in the Second World War, hence the soldiers and planes. The main character in The Wall’s storyline goes by the name of Pink, and you’re probably right in that Pink resembles Syd in a way. The songs that deal with moments of personal stress especially bring Syd’s psychotic behaviour to mind. But what do you think of the album, Sport? I don’t think I’ve ever actually asked you.”

“Musically, I think it’s far too gloomy and tense and I find it all a bit incoherent. It’s also way too aggressive, for my taste. You?”

“I like the concept, but most of all I think there are some

great musical moments on it, including my most favourite guitar solo ever. Comfortably Numb has to be one of the best guitar anthems of all time, and it still sounds great now. It's a bit like a Jimmy Page or a Hendrix solo, you know with the first note what song it is. I still get goose bumps every time I listen to it. And you can play air guitar to it pretty accurately. Which is the ultimate test, of course. You wait and see. I'm not sure who's going to play that solo tonight, though. Snowy White, probably."

"Who?"

"Snowy White," I laughed.

"There's a guy in the band called Snowy White?"

"There sure is. His actual name is Terence Charles White. I don't know who gave him the name Snowy. He played with Thin Lizzy and had a huge solo hit in the early eighties, called Bird of Paradise. He's one of the nicest blokes I've ever met. And a talented guitar player, too."

By now the concert area was one enormous sea of people. I'd never been to such a well-attended event. It was impossible to estimate how many people were here, but it was an imposing sight. Sport seemed to read my mind.

"Pretty awesome, isn't it?" he said.

"You're damn right. Glad we don't have to stand in the middle of all that."

"Don't see myself getting us beers in that crowd either," he chuckled.

Getting up from his seat, Sport excused himself to the people sitting next to us and went off to fetch some refreshments. I placed my elbows on my knees and, with my chin on my hands, gazed silently at the scenery in front of me. Pretty awesome indeed.

Sport returned with two large, German-sized plastic glasses of beer.

"Do you consider The Wall to be the last of the great classic Pink Floyd albums?" he asked, tilting his head inquisitively while still sipping his beer.

"Yes, possibly. The Final Cut was more or less a Roger Waters solo effort, including a lot of leftovers from The Wall. There are a couple of great songs on it, but you can hardly call it a classic album. Musically, The Wall is a farewell to the seventies. Give me any genre of popular music and I dare to say that its best albums were made in the seventies. The Wall sort of closes the curtains on all that. The end of an era with the best popular music ever. Better than the crap we've been forced to listen to over the last ten years."

"I like the stuff from the sixties, too," Sport said. "But I totally agree about the last few years. Hard to find any albums from the eighties I like. Although there are a few exceptions, of course."

"I like progressive bands like Marillion, It Bites and Saga. Rush has recently released some great stuff, too. But if you listen to the later Pink Floyd, Genesis and Yes releases, well, let's just say they're not exactly their best work, if you ask me."

"Progressive rock is soooooo boring!" Sport said, yawning.

"Don't forget I've introduced you to Prince, the other day. He's doing some crazy stuff, too. The way he incorporates jazz, soul and funk into pop music is pretty out of the box. I have no problem calling that progressive as well."

"OK. Now we're getting somewhere. What was the name of that Pink Floyd album, again? The one without Roger Waters?"

"A Momentary Lapse Of Reason?"

"Yes. That one sucked big time, didn't it?"

"Hm, it's not one of my favourites. It feels too constructed. It lacks the edge and soul of Pink Floyd and the anger and sharpness of Roger Waters' creativity. The songs are pretty poor, but I am glad David is back playing some brilliant guitar again."

"Do you think it was wise of them to continue after Waters left?"

"Well...."

Before I could answer Sport's question, I was saved by the bell. Or rather, a whistle. It was ten o'clock and Leonard Cheshire, the wartime pilot with the charity fund, opened the concert with a brief speech and a blow on a World War II whistle.

The start was nothing short of dramatic. The sound was horrible, and some sort of problem meant the performers had to stop and restart at least twice in the first quarter of the show. I felt sorry for the artists who had to go through the ordeal. The Scorpions kicked off the whole thing and went completely over the top in their glorious AOR-style: fireworks included. They just ignored all the technical hiccups and got on with it. But for poor Ute Lemper, a well-known German singer, having to deal with the technical issues in front of her home crowd was clearly a pain.

Fortunately, things got better as the evening progressed and there were some impressive moments with Sinead O'Connor singing Mother and Van Morrison doing Comfortably Numb. Bryan Adams' version of Young Lust and Paul Carrack's Hey You, singing out of sight behind the wall, were excellent. Joni Mitchell and Thomas Dolby were not. Cyndi Lauper was quite embarrassing. In front of the white mega wall, Roger Waters took the role of Pink and performed alone mostly, or with extras as props, including Gerald Scarfe's inflatables, which towered 15 meters above the wall. The chilling highlight came when the entire crowd chanted "tear down the wall!" at the top of their lungs. When the polystyrene blocks finally came tumbling down, they roared long and massively. The show officially ended with The Tide Is Turning, a song from Waters' recent Radio K.A.O.S. It felt like an anti-climax, and most were people already leaving.

With the whole thing over, I poked Sport with my elbow. His eyes looked weird and glazed over.

"And?" I asked.

"That was pretty awful, wasn't it?"

We got up and fought our way to the exits. At least it gave me some time to make up my mind.

"I'm not sure 'awful' is the right adjective," I countered after a couple of minutes' thought. "I agree that it was a bit disappointing, but I think we just witnessed a historic event. For me, the place and time make it impressive. For Roger Waters, his biggest achievement is that he timed this gig to perfection."

We made our way through a silent crowd; it was as if everyone was mentally digesting the last couple of hours. Sport, of course, had made his mind up hours ago and had no such problems.

"It's not the immense size of this place, here at Potsdamer Platz. And it's not the size of the crowd either. It's to do with the number of so-called famous artists Roger Waters needed to draw attention to his brainchild. It was a poor parade of rock stars, all wanting a piece of the action. I completely lost the meaning and original intention of The Wall. He could have announced the coming of Jesus or the start of World War III and we wouldn't have noticed. The message was smothered by poor execution, all good intentions not withstanding."

▪ ▪ ▪

As we walked over the Schöneberger Ufer along the canal, I quietly mulled over Sport's remark about a 'poor parade of rock stars'. I didn't agree on the 'poor' part, but I questioned the number of artists that were deemed necessary to make this circus a success. What is it that draws the ordinary public to successful people and stardom, anyway? Is a couple of hours stargazing an excuse to escape reality? Is the quality of our lives measured by the number of minutes we appear on TV or the amount of money we have in the bank? And what makes someone who collects rubbish for a living so very different from a person who is born with a talent for singing or acting?

My head was overflowing with questions. Neither Sport nor Roger Waters had helped me find the answers tonight.

44
A BOAT LIES WATING

The Astoria, River Thames at Hampton, March 2, 1994

Leaving the hum of the traffic on Hampton Court Road behind me, I closed the door in the huge brick wall to find myself in a lush green haven of tranquillity. The impeccably kept garden was idyllic, with a huge orangery nestled in the trees, a swathe of manicured lawn and a beautiful Edwardian-style houseboat moored on the river Thames at the bottom. The contrast in scenery and sudden lack of engine noise quite threw me and it took me a few seconds to adjust.

Coming round, I saw a woman with long dark hair walking to meet me. She smiled but didn't introduce herself.

"You must be Matt?"

A funny thing to ask since I'd just announced my arrival through the intercom.

"I am. Thanks for letting me in. I'm here to see David, he's expecting me."

The woman smiled again and turning, led me towards the oversized greenhouse which, as we got closer, I realised was more like a regular house. She showed me into a kind of enormous of living room full of plants and an assortment of cupboards and desks. There were various open lounge areas spread around the space and I was pointed toward a large sofa surrounded by windows overlooking the far end of the garden.

"Make yourself comfortable. Can I get you anything?"

"A cup of tea would be great, thanks. Black, please. With sugar."

"Coming right up. They'll be with you shortly."

Wondering who she meant by 'they', I picked up a copy of Country Living from the pile of magazines scattered on the small table in front of me and, tea in hand, settled back to wait. Less than 15 minutes later, I looked up to see a familiar face walking towards me. It wasn't Dave Gilmour but his long-time guitar tech Phil Taylor.

"Phil! What a fantastic surprise!"

We hugged, like old mates do.

"Matt, you ol' tosser," Phil grinned. "Good to see you again."

Phil had been a dedicated and loyal crew member for as long as I can remember. I liked him a lot. Fun to hang around with, always good for a couple of marvellous stories and never ever disrespectful towards his employer. I always made sure I said 'hi' to him whenever I joined Pink Floyd on tour. Sometimes we'd sit and chat after soundcheck or at the hotel bar when the crew wasn't travelling by bus. We weren't close friends, but I enjoyed his company and I hadn't seen him for at least fifteen years. In no time Phil and I were exchanging pleasantries like it was yesterday.

"David's busy with the new release and the tour that starts at end of this month. He still has a couple of phone calls to make and said to tell you he'd be done in about twenty minutes. Mind if I keep you company?"

"No, not at all. You can fill me in on the album and the boat. I know the band sometimes recorded here, but I've never actually seen it 'in the flesh' if you like."

"I'll give you a quick tour later," Phil said.

"That would be great!"

"David told me you're working on the book, again. Is that good or bad news for us?"

"Depends which side you're on," I laughed. "I had some trouble getting motivated after all the goings on with last album. I didn't want to have to choose sides, for one. I also needed to avoid getting all entangled in a legal battle, and wasn't sure what I could and couldn't write anymore. But, yes, here I am, back on track."

"Does Roger know you're writing, again?" Phil asked.

"Not yet, but I'm planning to let him and the rest of the guys proofread the book before I even consider sending it to publishers. And, let's not forget it was Roger's idea in the first place."

"Good luck with that, Matt. I'm not sure either David or Roger wants you to publish anything at this point. There's still some animosity between the two of them, probably more than either of us know."

"All I can do is hope they've learned to trust me over the years." I said. "I won't write anything they don't absolutely consent to. But this is exactly why it's been taking me so long. It's felt like walking a tightrope, and I've had enough of it. From now on, I'm going to write what I want to write. I'll deal with the fallout when they read it. That probably won't be for another year, anyway."

"I wish you every success, man. I really do. If anyone can pull this off, it's you. Don't let those grumpy old men stand in your way. They know you and that gives you a head start. I'm sure it'll work out fine. Now, let's talk about the Astoria. What do you want to know?"

I was right to like this guy. Those were kind words. I'd

heard a fair amount about the Astoria in the band's context, but from the glimpse I'd got of her on the water, I thought she was the most opulent houseboat I'd ever seen. I was keen to know her story, and who better to tell it than Phil? I asked if he'd give me a short rundown on the boat's history.

"The Astoria was built in 1911 by Fred Karno, an old-time comedian and veteran of the English vaudeville circuit. The story goes Karno got his break into show business after working out at a gym he was doing a plumbing job for. It turned out the lad was a born athlete. After winning a bunch of prizes and a stint as an acrobat in a circus, he got into pantomime and then set up the Karno Company with Charlie Chaplin and Stan Laurel no less. They sold out music halls up and down the country with their pie-in-the-face slapstick acts, a type of comedy no one had seen before. Karno was a bit of an eccentric ladies' man. He wanted the best, most lavish houseboat on the river permanently anchored alongside his extravagant new hotel, The Karsino, on Tagg's Island. He paid 7000 quid, a fortune in those days, to have the finest craftsmen available build her. When music hall died out and Karno went bankrupt, he sold the Astoria to another vaudeville veteran, Vesta Victoria. The song Daddy Wouldn't Buy Me A Bow-Wow is one of hers. After she died, the boat was bought by a Sir James Greenwood. Unlike the previous owners, he wasn't a showbiz man. He was a writer and journalist like you, but he loved music and the grand gesture. One time he had an entire 90-piece orchestra play from Astoria's deck. Over 2000 people attended the concert. There was a grand firework display, the lot. They moored boats from here all the way over to the far riverbank, they say."

"That's a great story," I said, fishing out my notebook and scribbling down a few notes for later. I'd decided it wasn't the right time to pull out a recorder.

"Isn't it just? Would be great to do a book on the Astoria someday. We've already got quite a collection of photos and some other bits and pieces about her history."

Phil pointed to a building outside.

"You see that house over there? That's Hampton Villa. It's all apartments now, but it used to belong to the celebrated 18th century actor, playwright and theatre manager, David Garrick. Garrick's the man who brought Shakespeare to the masses. The domed folly in the garden there, is a temple Garrick erected to Shakespeare. Apart from theatre, Garrick loved grand houses and especially the one at Hampton. The garden was famous even in his day; it has featured in quite a few famous paintings from that time. Back then, these grounds were all part of David Garrick's garden."

"And the building we're sitting in?"

"This used to be a conservatory. Now we use it as our kitchen, bathroom and lounge."

"David bought the boat in 1986, right?"

"Correct. The Astoria was only five minutes away from where he lived. We saw it was for sale, so just out of interest, me, David and Warrick, a Floyd roadie, went and had a look at it. In the car, after having been shown around, we all agreed that it was an absolutely wonderful place and that he should buy it. It wasn't expensive at all, but at first David had no idea what he could use it for. It was such a fabulous place. Through the years, David had always had a home studio, but the house he was living in at the time was too small. His equipment was all in storage. After a bit of thought, he realised the houseboat would be a great place to be creative in and so he bought it, initially as somewhere he could go to write music."

"What kind of shape was it in?"

"Unbelievably, the boat was in great condition considering its age. It was beautifully furnished. There was a caretaker living on board, so it was always well looked after."

"Must have been quite a challenge to keep the original design intact when you converted it into a modern studio?"

"From the start, our goal was to keep the charm and feel of the place. But turning a beautiful houseboat into a fantastic control room and studio had its challenges for sure. It's not like you can knock down walls and rebuild them, you have to work with what's there. Fortunately, the boat is built of wood throughout, so most of it was straightforward. We could take the floors up and there was enough room underneath for us to run the audio and mains cabling up and down the boat without sawing holes everywhere."

"Who did you involve for the acoustics?"

"A guy named Nick Whittaker, an acoustician who'd done a couple of other things for us in the past. We still use him now. But there's been a constant stream of people. Also a few you might remember, James Guthrie and Andy Jackson, for example. They're both fantastic engineers and they have great ears. Andy used to be James' assistant at the Utopia studios in London in the mid-seventies, by the way. But along with Nick Whittaker and his measuring equipment, I guess it's me who has been the main driving force and motivator."

"Do you allow people other than the band in here to record?"

"It is not a commercial studio in the normal sense, if that's what you mean. It's David's private studio. When he's not here, we do sometimes let friends and acquaintances use it. But we're not in any studio directories and we never advertise. It's still really private. David is quite happy closing it down in the periods when he's not working. So, there's no pressure and it's all very low-key and discreet."

▪ ▪ ▪

The woman who'd brought us tea arrived to announce David was ready to see me. We stood up and with Phil leading the way, left the greenhouse, walked down to the Astoria and stepped a century back in time. Following a very narrow mahogany-lined passageway, we reached one of the recording rooms at the far end of the boat where we found David Gilmour reading through a bunch of papers.

"Don't sign those contracts! You may want a higher percentage," I quipped.

David looked up and laughed. "Seems my new attorney has arrived!" he retorted in his characteristically soft voice.

We shook hands and David gestured for me to sit down next to him on the beige coach. The control was built in the main living room on the boat and had windows overlooking the river on two sides and across the riverside garden on the third. I watched a pair of swans glide gracefully past.

"I'll leave you guys to it. Let me know when you're done and I'll be more than happy to take you on the guided tour I promised," Phil excused himself and left.

"Good to see you again. It's been quite a while. How are you doing?" David asked, politely.

"Not too bad, thanks. Glad you have some time to see me."

"My pleasure, Matt."

"Would you mind if I get the recorder out?" I asked, getting straight to business.

"No, not at all, go ahead. But tell me, what's happening with the book? I hear you're back to writing again?"

"Yes," I nodded. "It took me a long time to get my motivation back. Thanks to the new album, I'm giving it another try. I want to let you know though that I won't publish a word without your full consent."

"Thanks, Matt. I appreciate that. There's still a lot of rubbish written about us, but I'm confident that I can trust you on this."

I pushed Record.

"It's a stunning place you have here. Phil just told me a bit of its history."

"It's beautiful, isn't it? And a wonderfully comfortable, ninety feet long working environment."

"How did you find out about the Astoria?"

"Well, I was driving around here one day, I guess it was 1986. I'd been banned from driving for a year, so I was being driven rather than driving myself, and I was looking out of the windows a lot more. I spotted some kind of metal works sticking out over the top over a brick wall and asked my chauffeur to pull over so I could take a look. When I peered over, I saw this incredible boat. And I thought 'Oh, that's fantastic.' About two weeks later, when I was in the dentist waiting room, I picked up a Country Life and there it was: For Sale. I rang them up, came down, had a look, and bought it. I didn't even think about putting a studio in it at first. It was just an exceptionally beautiful place."

"You must have been over the moon."

"I was. And I still am. It's so lovely to be here. To have the water gently drifting past and all that. And the windows! I like to have windows. I've spent too much time in studios and most of them don't have windows. I can't stand being in places that don't have windows anymore."

"A Momentary Lapse Of Reason was the first album you recorded here?"

"It was. We used it for the early stages of the recording. Later, Bob Ezrin wanted us to move to Los Angeles because he needed a bigger studio. That's where we recorded the parts with Jim Keltner, Vinny Appice, Tom Scott and Bill Payne."

"How did the ball start rolling again? And how did you get Rick back in?"

"In 1986, I tried to consolidate the writing I'd done into

some sort of shape. To get an idea of whether I could make an album. I didn't want to bring out the old stuff for nostalgic reasons only. Nick and I had to put the money in to fund it all. I had enough, but Nick had to put his Ferrari GTO down as collateral. Obviously, we could have borrowed money, but then we would have had to share the profits, and we were confident that we would do OK. At some point in the proceedings, Rick expressed an interest in being part of it. We thought it a great idea, and that was that really. There were one or two legal reasons which made it a little tricky. We talked, argued and negotiated, and now he's on a percentage of everything, not just the record. Nick and I had put up all the money and had taken all the risks on everything, including the lawsuits with Roger. When you take all the risks, you expect to get more of the profits, quite simply."

"Was it an easy or difficult album to write and record?"

"It was an arduous process. We were all kind of catatonic. Unfortunately, we didn't really work together an awful lot. But the success of the album, the follow-up tour and the enjoyment we got from working together meant that we could do things differently."

"Where you worried about any criticism from Roger at the time?"

"No, not for a second. I knew he wasn't going to like A Momentary Lapse. Of course he was going to say he hated it. It was inevitable. How could he like it?"

I wasn't sure how much David was willing to talk about Roger, but I tried anyway.

"What's the status on the feud between you and Roger? Still not on speaking terms?"

David sighed.

"Look, I don't share Roger's sense of angst about music and the world. If I did, maybe we would have been able to agree on our dispute. While Roger's acted dumbly and isolated himself, I've somehow garnered new strength out of the extra workload I've had this last year."

"I remember reading that Roger had said: 'Go on, go ahead, you'll never get it together, you wankers.'"

"That's what he said. I was in the room."

"Then again, time heals many wounds. But not yours, yet..."

"It's impossible for us to be friends now, but we never have been. Nick was always much closer to Roger than I ever was. But we could have sorted this whole business out enough for us to work together on a reasonable, tolerable level. We could have made room for each other if there'd been any sort of mutual respect. But Roger spent the last years deliberately trying to wreck us. There's no doubt that that's what he has been doing. In all the interviews he gave, he was conducting a vicious wrecking campaign, and I cannot remain friendly with someone like that."

"Most of it happened in the years following the release of A Momentary Lapse. He's been reasonably quiet of late. Can't the both of you bury the hatched and move on?"

"I think he's got my phone number and I've got his. But I have no interest in discussing anything with him. He's told too many lies and too many bad things have happened. I'm not very good at holding grudges for any length of time, but he's done some terrible things. Honesty is not one of the things that he will let get in the way of his pursuit of power."

"And now there's a new album out," I said, trying to change the subject and mood.

"We kicked off in January last year. Nick, myself, Rick, and Guy Pratt, the bass player from our last tour, went into the Britannia Row studios and jammed away for two weeks, playing whatever was in our heads or making things up on the spot. We then all trouped over to the Astoria and started listening to the tapes and working stuff out. It turned out we had 65 pieces of music! We arranged those 65 pieces according to how popular they were among us. Gradually, we merged some and scrapped others until eventually we had between 11 and 15 songs that we all liked."

"Quite a different approach, compared to the last one," I remarked.

"Rick, Nick and I worked together as a unit in a way that we hadn't done for many, many years. The Division Bell has an overarching cohesiveness to it. It sounds like we all meant it and that we're all in synch with each other. The whole thing is very much a joint effort, far more than A Momentary Lapse Of Reason ever was."

"Who was in charge of the lyrics, this time 'round?"

"Well, a lot of the lyrics resulted from a collaboration between myself and my girlfriend..."

"... Girlfriend?" I queried a bit cheekily, knowing that David and Ginger had divorced a few years back.

"Her name is Polly," David grinned. "We've been seeing each other for a couple of years now. Polly's at the heart of everything we do. She's my partner in life and writes most of the lyrics, too. In the beginning, she tried not to interfere at all and encouraged me to do it all on my own. But as time went by and the process absorbed me 24/7, she got more and more involved. First, she only worked on writing lyrics, but then she got drawn into the whole music process. It's been nice to work with her and have input from someone who had no ambition to write pop songs. I imagine it was good for Polly to discover her brain could function musically, even though she had no musical skills. Her help was invaluable... And speaking of invaluable help..."

I followed David's sparkling eyes and turned my head. Behind me, the dark-haired woman who'd met me in the garden was holding a tray with a teapot and some cups.

"Matt, meet Polly. Polly, meet Matt."

"We've already met, darling," Polly said, putting the tray on the table in front of us. "Black with sugar, if I'm not mistaken."

"Yes, thank you," I said politely. "And please, feel free to join us, if you like."

"OK, but only for a minute then. I don't want to ruin your interview."

"So, Polly, be truthful, what has it been like, working with David?" I asked her candidly.

She smiled. "To be honest, I'd had never felt nervous about writing before, but when I found myself, a 30-year-old woman, writing songs for a band of blokes in their mid-40's, I felt like I was sticking my head above a very particular parapet."

"You had some huge shoes to fill," I noted, winking at David.

"Believe it, or not," Polly replied, "I'm a proper fan of Roger Waters' lyrics. He always finds the right image to illustrate a point. Not that I've ever set out to replace him as Pink Floyd's chief wordsmith."

"There's absolutely no reason she shouldn't. She can write," David added. "I don't recall ever saying to Roger: 'God, these lyrics are fucking brilliant!' But they were. And I should have done."

"It's so strange," Polly says, shaking her head. "These guys should have so much to say to each other. But truly, they never speak. Then they start playing and there's this incredible conversation. My greatest challenge is convincing this guy to write for himself."

"Melodies just descend and swirl around in my mind without me having to try," David said, trying to explain himself. "I get pathetically stuck with words. My brain just closes. It's maddening."

Polly stood up and raised her arms to the sky in theatrical despair. "How will he ever write me a love song? See you guys soon."

As Polly left the control room, David leaned slightly forward.

"I'll share a secret with you if you absolutely promise to keep it quiet," he whispered.

"Sure, man. No problem."

"I proposed to Polly a little while back. We're going to get married soon, and Storm is going to be my best man."

"That's splendid news! Congratulations. When's the great day?"

"In July. We're trying to squeeze the wedding in between the new tour, but we'll have to postpone our honeymoon."

"Glad you're happy. The two of you seem to be a perfect match."

"Thanks. And she's bringing an addition to the family. Polly's got a little son called Charlie. He's a bright young kid, almost five years old. You'll hear him talking on the phone to Steve on the new album, at the end of High Hopes."

"What's it like for him having a second dad around?"

"He was used to having just his mum, since his dad doesn't show himself much. But Charlie's fantastic. He liked me at first, but when he realised that it was getting serious, he had a little change of heart. It's not bad at all, he's just careful. He doesn't give himself away to people cheaply or lightly. Polly and I are like that, too. We're not over-approachable and don't leap into friendships with both feet. We're wary and take our time."

"You are quite the family man now, with four kids to look after."

"I love being a dad. It's full of frustrations and annoyances and stuff, but the significant moments are really just so great. They're all lovely. I hope to adopt Charlie as soon as possible. You know, Matt, family is everything. You have to devote time and yourself to raising children if that is what you elect to do with your life. So, yeah, I'm loving my life with my family. When I was a young man, ambition, the desire to be with these other guys in a band was more important. I was and still am very driven in what I do, it's just that my perspective on what is most important has changed. I can also prioritise my time better. So, what did you think of the new album?"

The next 15 minutes we spent talking about the songs on The Division Bell. The album wasn't due to be released until the end of the month, but they'd sent me a promo copy on cassette tape and already had the pleasure of listening to it. Phil returned and according to his word showed me around the other areas of the Astoria. David insisted on saying goodbye in person, so at the end of the tour, I went back to the control room.

David walked with me up through the garden back to the door I'd entered only two hours ago. It seemed longer.

"Thanks for taking the time to come and visit me here. As always, it was fun talking to you, Matt."

"The pleasure was all mine. Hope to see you on tour some time soon."

"Good luck with the writing and keep me in the loop, will you?"

"I will. Take care, David."

We shook hands and the man who had sold over 140 million albums worldwide opened the large wooden door to let me through.

"Please remember," he said, giving me one last piece of advice on my way out, "some things can't be expressed in words. Sometimes it's better to let the music do the talking."

55
COMING BACK TO LIFE

Hyde Park, London, July 2, 2005

At the end of an extraordinary night, Roger Waters made an extraordinary move. In front of an audience of millions, he held out his arm to David Gilmour and waved him over: a small gesture with a huge significance. Gilmour, who had just put down his black Strat, accepted the invitation and walked over to Waters. The four musicians stood side by side, arms around each other's shoulders and genuine radiant smiles on their faces. In the final few seconds of their short Live 8 set, David, Roger, Nick, and Richard were, literally, closer than they had been for ages. For a few brief moments, all animosity was gone and the four veterans silently acknowledged the mutual bond that, after 24 years, had brought them back together again.

It had been a magical day with a monumental ending. It lasted for only four songs and barely 25 minutes. Nobody wanted it to stop. We all knew the chances of a follow-up were slim, but the night had given us hope. I saw Polly smiling and hugging her children and lots of other familiar faces soaking in the atmosphere, sharing the emotions. The only person who was sadly missing was Steve O'Rourke. Steve had suffered a stroke and died two years ago. Shame he wasn't here to witness this. He would have been so proud of his boys.

I couldn't have been happier. For the last few days, I'd lived in a constant state of euphoria, and tonight I reached the pinnacle of joy. As soon as David had announced Pink Floyd was going to reunite on stage in Hyde Park, I was determined to get a ticket. The London line-up of the event also included Paul McCartney, the Who, Elton John, Madonna, R.E.M., U2, Coldplay and Robbie Williams, so I had more than one reason to look forward to it. And it only got better.

▪ ▪ ▪

Two weeks ago, out of the blue, Alan Timms, my former editor at Rock Parade, had called. I'd not spoken to Al in over 25 years. We briefly chatted and then he suddenly fired off a question: "Matt, am I right in assuming you still know a lot about Pink Floyd?" I gave him a quick rundown of my encounters with the band and confirmed that I did indeed know the guys slightly better than the average fan.

Timms was now running a video production company. Happy with my answer, he explained that he was looking for someone who could do some short post-Live 8 interviews with Roger, David, and Bob Geldof. The interviews would later be incorporated in a 'making of' documentary. I was more than happy to oblige, and before we knew it, we were discussing details. He would send me a pass so I'd be able to both fully enjoy the festivities and also meet with the video and production crew during the day. The actual interviews were set at two different London hotels a week after the big event.

As a result, earlier today, I'd met with Timms and his team. We'd gone over the timetables and all the specifics.

They'd also quickly approved the list of questions I'd drawn up for the three interviews. That wasn't hard to do since they knew perfectly well the various managements involved would oversee the final the edits, anyway. A bonus to this unique opportunity was that it had got me thinking about my book again. I asked Timms if I could use some filmed quotes for my little project and he saw no problems.

After jotting down a few logistical notes for the job ahead, I wandered off to make the most of my time backstage. They'd equipped the compound with green dressing trailers, catering, and a well-stocked bar. I'm not easily dazzled by meeting the odd rock celebrity, but Live 8 was turning out to be one major star fest, a veritable hotspot of celebs, important people and attention seeking wannabes. I saw Paul McCartney marching around with a camera crew, Sting and his wife behaving like movie stars and Bono working the backstage crowd, shaking lots of hands like a true politician.

Wearing my purple wristband, I strolled as nonchalantly as I could past the u-shaped Portakabins and over the next few hours, spotted Brad Pitt, David Beckham, Paris Hilton and John McEnroe. I even spied Bill Gates giving the occasional interview about poverty and Africa in full rock star fashion. At first, I wasn't completely sure what they were all doing here, but as the program progressed it became clear most had some sort of role in presenting the acts on stage.

It was funny to see how some journalists, managers and even other musicians turned into hysterical fans when in proximity to the stars. But the overall feeling was that today was all about happiness and joy, so nobody really cared. Personally, I found the upbeat atmosphere a bit surprising. Sir Bob was fighting poverty, and we were having the time of our lives. Oh well, as long as the money was pouring in, the end justified the means. Or so I hoped.

Wandering a bit aimlessly around the compound, I was

greeted by a smile and nod from David Gilmour who was making his way with Polly and kids to watch Elton John perform on stage. Now was not a good time for a catch-up. I had my hopes set on a brief 'hello' after Elton's set, but I saw him chatting away with Roger, something no one had seen in a long, long time. And I wasn't the only one staring at the scene in disbelief.

Not wanting to waste the remarkable moment, I went over to Tim Renwick who was sitting at a table and introduced myself. The grey veteran, goatee beard and all, looked bored out of his mind. Tim had worked with Rick on his Broken China album, played with Roger, and had been a key part of Pink Floyd's touring band from 1987 onwards.

"I was surprised to be asked," the guitarist said grinning. "I met David a few weeks ago. He told me he had categorically turned the opportunity down. Then the next thing I know, we're talking again and he calmly announces: 'We're doing it now, and we're doing it with Roger.' I never thought they would. Then David suddenly declares that 'it would be a real laugh' and here we are. It is actually going to happen!"

I asked Tim how rehearsals had gone after being apart for so many years.

"As you can imagine," he said wryly, "Roger wanted to be group leader from the start. I didn't feel too good about that. He didn't seem to give any credit to the fact that most of the musicians and crew had worked together on and off for years without his help. But you know, Roger is Roger, and it's still a great honour to be involved. I can't wait to get on stage tonight. It's going to be phenomenal for sure. It means quite a lot to me on a personal level too, as I played in Eric Clapton's band at the original Live Aid concert in Philadelphia twenty years ago!"

"Wow, to be part of such a historic event, not once but

twice. That is very special," I said, duly impressed. "Still, it must be a bit weird, with you knowing both David and Roger so well."

"In a way it is, but we're all trying to keep our heads down and just get on with our own gig. Roger and I went to the same school, and I played in his band on the Pros And Cons-tour, so I have some previous experience of his band-leading style. I have tremendous respect for him. He's a very clever man, but he is also profoundly serious. Don't tell him I said so, but Roger is pretty boring to work for. He likes everything to be the same, night after night. David is generally far more fun. That's one reason I trusted he knew what he was doing when he agreed to the reunion. We'll see how it all works out soon enough."

According to Tim, Roger had proposed including In the Flesh and Run Like Hell in the set, but the others thought the songs too confrontational and wouldn't have it. They settled for Breathe, Money, Wish You Were Here and Comfortably Numb. Apart from Tim, keyboardist Jon Carin, saxophonist Dick Parry and backup singer Carol Kenyon would join the band on stage.

I asked how far he and David went back.

"Phew, let me think... We both were born and grew up in Cambridge and played in local bands. David played in a group called Jokers Wild. They did harmonic Hollies-style versions of chart hits, a bit like The Beach Boys and Four Seasons. They were quite good, probably the best group in Cambridge. At some point Willie Wilson replaced the original drummer, then Rick Wills, later of Foreigner, took over on bass and when David moved to London. They went with him and formed The Flowers. The trio went off to try their luck in France and when that didn't work out, they came back to the UK and David joined Pink Floyd. All us musicians tend to stay in touch, you know, and I'd played with Rick in a band called Little Women for a while. After I asked Rick to join my band Quiver some time later, we saw David quite a lot. He'd occasionally jam with us and we rehearsed in his home studio and recorded a few demos there. Around that time, we were being managed Steve O'Rourke and we often opened for the Floyd. Quiver eventually joined forces with The Sutherland Brothers..."

"...Arms Of Mary!"

"Exactly! We never lost the connection with David. He later produced and played pedal steel guitar on a B-side of ours, called We Get Along. Throughout this time, I think I saw every Floyd tour that there was!"

"That's quite a story, Tim. I'm going to look up Quiver and buy some of your music when I get home."

"Cool, man. Hope you'll like it."

"How did you end up playing with Pink Floyd in 1987?"

"David called me out of the blue and asked if I'd like to play with the band. I was completely gobsmacked. I'd played some acoustic guitar on the soundtrack of The Wall, but apart from that I had no other experience of playing with the band. I toured with them non-stop for 16 months and I had a great time."

Suddenly our eyes were drawn to a blonde woman in a white suit who was so scintillating sexy she'd brought everything and everybody to a stop. Madonna was making her way to the stage. I wasn't a big fan of her music, but this was an opportunity not to be missed.

"Go," Tim said, reading my mind. "I'll probably be joining you in a minute."

I stood up, shook Tim's hand, and wished him a great time on stage.

Madonna's performance was rather disappointing, but Sting, Robbie Williams and The Who were nothing less than brilliant. In fact, most acts were superb. It was as if, knowing what was at stake, they were playing their hearts out to inspire people around the globe to raise funds for famine relief and make poverty history.

When Pink Floyd came on at 11 pm, there were no signs of tension in the band, and for a moment it seemed like time had warped us back to happier days. We all felt thirty years younger, artists probably included. Memories came flashing back, and some people were visibly fighting back tears of happiness. The lucky ones in the golden circle in front of the stage, the 200.000 people in Hyde Park, and the millions watching at home all understood the huge significance of this historic performance.

The last notes of Comfortably Numb would have been a perfect ending to a perfect day, were it not for Paul McCartney who at the last moment surprised us all with an unannounced appearance by George Michael for Drive My Car and a cool version of Helter Skelter. As the assembled musicians gathered for an extended encore of Hey Jude, everybody knew that Live 8 had been a remarkable once-in-a-lifetime event.

▪ ▪ ▪

Two days later, on July 4, HMV reported that sales of Pink Floyd albums had increased thirteenfold since Live 8. David Gilmour quickly announced that he would donate all royalties from the rise in album sales to charity and encouraged other artists to do the same. And while everybody was still on a high from the festivities in Hyde Park, London won its bid to host the 2012 Olympic Games and the cheering began all over again.

With spirits suitably elevated, I was really looking forward to doing my interviews in a few days' time. That came to an abrupt end when on July 7, at the end of the morning rush hour, a series of coordinated suicide bombings targeting commuters travelling on the city's public transport system killed 52 people and injured 700 more. It was Britain's deadliest terrorist incident since Lockerbie. As a result, they postponed the interviews for a week and moved to a suite at the fancy Mandarin Oriental Hyde Park at Knightsbridge.

▪ ▪ ▪

Later than planned, I saw Bob Geldof being fitted with a small microphone. The greetings and introduction were open and pleasant. Saint Bob is the sort of person who makes you feel quickly at ease. Like me, he was probably still drawing on the positive energy that had abounded in the city before the attacks. This was my first ever interview on video, but I was completely calm, no nerves whatsoever. We first talked about the bombings, which, of course, he condemned outright. Then the lights were switched on, the cameras started rolling, and we found ourselves right back in Live 8-mode. Bob moved to the edge of his chair and I dropped the first question.

"Why did you decide to time Live 8 around the G8 summit?"

"This G8 is taking place in the UK. A lot of the G8 guys are on their last political legs: Schroeder's going to lose in Germany, Chirac won't stand because he knows he will lose, Berlusconi has a year left at most, Canada's Paul Martin is clinging on by a thread, George Bush can't stand again, and Tony Blair said he wouldn't. It gives us a chance to appeal to their sense of legacy. Combined with all this, our generation has become the Establishment. I've called Bono the rock god of the Establishment before. And me? I'm just a paddy with a hat on."

"Are you happy with the results and the awareness Live 8 raised?"

"Yes, I am. It reverberated politically and socially, inspired the leaders and a future generation. We jumped on a stage again and asked for some money to stop people dying of hunger. It has now become a topic of global politics and it is pursued by the global activist movement."

"Let's go back to the moment of initial contact with Pink Floyd. What was the first thing you did to get them interested in performing at Live 8?"

"Around May," Bob Geldof recalled, "I rang David Gilmour. I asked him if he was willing to put Pink Floyd back together. He's said no because he was in the middle of his solo album. I suggested going down to see him and got on a train. But when I was at East Croydon, I got a call from David saying 'Bob, there's no point, get off the train.' I replied that I was coming down anyway."

"Then what happened?"

"I arrived at his farm and explained the whole plan in detail. David was still being pig-headed, insisting that 'You've got enough prominent people; you don't need us.' But I could see he felt awful about saying no. When he drove me back to the station, I made him promise to think about it."

"You must have had more tricks up your sleeve..."

"Yes, I rang Nick Mason," Geldof said, laughing. "He was unaware of my plans. We knew each other from social and charity events we'd been involved in after The Wall. I told him about the event and that David had said no. Nick explained that David didn't want to re-group Pink Floyd for Live 8 for good reason: the band was not in a working state."

"Did you ask Nick to persuade David?"

"I did, but he refused. Because, and I quote him here: 'you

can take a horse to water but you can't make it drink; in David's case, you can't even get him near the water.' I thought that was pretty funny, but it didn't help the cause."

"You then called Roger?"

"Nick e-mailed Roger initially and gave him my number. Roger called me the next day. He was positive about the idea of playing together again for an event that was politically in tune with his own sentiments. He gave it some thought and called me back two weeks later. To my surprise, he asked me for David's phone number. Roger, bless his heart, convinced David to do it, and David made sure Rick Wright got back on board. David then issued a statement in which he said that 'any squabbles Roger and the band have had in the past are so petty in the context of Live 8'. I couldn't have been happier. Reforming Pink Floyd would bring even more attention to the event."

"Somebody told me they thought about involving Syd Barrett, as well..."

"I believe they played with the idea of asking him, but that didn't appear to be feasible. One paper reported that Syd's sister, Rosemary, had asked him what he thought about the reunion, and apparently he'd not reacted at all. 'He's no longer Syd, he's Roger now' she said. There is no contact and Syd doesn't want them to get in touch with him. You have to respect that."

"All this went on less than a month before the event?"

"They started planning meetings at London's Connaught Hotel right away. They did three days of rehearsals, which began on June 28, if I'm not mistaken. At West London's Black Island studios. One final rehearsal took place on July 1 in Hyde Park. They were a bit agitated about Madonna's rehearsal running late. Hyde Park was closing at 11 pm and the band was left with just half an hour. I remember there were about 25 workers in high-visibility jackets putting the barrier up at the front, and they all just stopped and stared and went into raucous applause at the end. We all knew by then that this was going to work out fine. As they came off stage, it looked as if they were walking on air. After that, all four of Pink Floyd and their wives went out for dinner together."

And with that, the interview was over. Geldof had to rush off to his next appointment and he left with his personal assistant. With two hours to kill before my next interview, I went for a bite to eat and before I knew it, Roger was sitting in the same chair Bob had occupied just a little earlier in the day.

▪ ▪ ▪

Roger and I had not seen each other in person since my visit to the Super Bear Studios in 1979. Apart from the occasional phone call, letter or fax about the book, we'd lost touch and, unfortunately, I never got hold of his private e-mail address. I had hoped to exchange a few words backstage at Hyde Park, but quickly realised it was not the right time or place for a little personal reunion.

It turned out I did not need to feel nervous because Roger greeted me like the old friend I hoped I still was. Being uncharacteristically polite, he asked how I was doing, and I gave him a less than one minute rundown of my life over the last 25 years. I complimented him on the Live 8 performance and, like Bob, he expressed his grief and disgust about the recent bombings. Then, after make-up and a quick soundcheck, the cameras started rolling again.

"Bob Geldof just told me a bit how he brought the four of you back together for Live 8. That was quite an achievement. Can you take me back to the rehearsals?"

"It was bound to be a bit tensed up, after all the history. But I went into the process, determined to roll over if there was an argument. I knew how to work this. If there's conflict, I immediately play dead. Then everything will be fine. And I did. It seemed to work rather well, I have to say."

"Can't you play dead a little longer? Say for an entire tour?"

"No. It isn't my natural style. I have far too much life and exuberance and attachment to the work, and far too many ideas. My natural state is to constantly express my ideas and feelings, sometimes at full volume. To not be engaged is a very alien condition for me."

"Who took the lead during rehearsals?"

"I was sort of controlling the whole thing, doing nothing. It was like walking on rice paper. I think it was a bit of a worry to David. I'm not sure if he gets how important the symbiosis between the four of us was during the golden years of the band. We were great together. We all contributed, but it was the combination of the four separate talents. It was a very, very special thing. The moment we plugged in for the first rehearsal, it was like putting on an old shoe."

"Do you feel you had to set things straight at Live 8? To prove you're on the right side of the Floyd history?"

"I've rolled over for Live 8 but I won't roll over forever. The press is to blame here because it wants a juicy tale. Syd was a juicy tale, and that is why his influence seems to be much bigger than it was in reality: he barely was a year in the band, and we have made our best work without him. That I wanted to dissolve the band also was a juicy tale. But I was also the one who immediately promised to play on Live 8. Dave, as you've been already made aware, first said 'no' to Bob Geldof. I am very political aware. It has always irritated Dave that I wrote intelligent, engaged lyrics concerning morality, ethics, and politics. He hated The Final Cut because I had put in too many references to Margaret Thatcher. Anyway, Live 8 was once again the proof that our music does a lot to people."

"How was it for you, standing up here with the guys after all these years?"

"It was quite emotional. Anyway, we were doing this for everyone who was not there, and particularly of course for Syd. A huge number of people saw us on TV, and I think it gave them an opportunity to reconnect with us. I think through the years they perceived me as the grumpy guy who left in a huff. After Live 8 I think they went 'Well, maybe he's not so grumpy after all'."

"So, you enjoyed it?"

"I absolutely did. I came to it with an open mind and an open heart and decided to just get on with it and do it. So maybe that changed people's perceptions to some extent. I'm thankful that we did it together, that the four of us got to draw some kind of line under it. Things have got better between David and me. We don't see each other socially, but yeah, there's no fussing and fighting going on."

"Would you do it again?"

"I've been thinking about having The Wall performed by Cirque du Soleil for a while now, but after Live 8 I think it would be great to play The Dark Side Of The Moon live, as well. I think we would need a special occasion for this. Whatever the reason for a sequel will be, we won't do it for the money."

"Is David on the same page as you?"

"He is very reluctant. It's been his baby for quite a few years now. He doesn't want to give up that position. Why should he? If we could somehow set our egos aside and come together for a reason and maybe do a few gigs in London, a few in New York and a few in LA, Palestine, wherever, I'd be up for it. It wouldn't be a one-off gig, because to do all that work just for one night wouldn't be worth it. But a number of events that would draw a line nicely under the work the four of us did together would be very satisfying for me. I'd be prepared to give six months or so in terms of preparation for something like that. I'm sure Nick would as well, but I don't think Dave wants to."

"Suppose it never happens, how would you like to be remembered?"

"As somebody who spoke his truth, stood by it through thick and thin and wasn't to be diverted by the vagaries of fashion or popularity or anything else. I paint what I see. When I left Pink Floyd in 1985, I allowed myself to be drawn into the public debate and saying unpleasant things about the other guys. If I'd been wise, I'd have kept my mouth shut. It was kind of ugly and I regret that."

"But then again, you're not retiring from music just yet..."

"It has been a huge revelation to discover that there's a young audience out there who love my work. I had no idea, really. And I've discovered changes in my personality. I no longer feel even faintly constrained to spit at anyone, to feel angry. How much longer I'll go on doing it, I don't know, but I do work every day. When I get those e-mails from my PR that tell me I've come third in some poll somewhere, I have to own up to a little glow of pride. There may be one of two exceptions, but most musicians are pretty insecure. And we crave that kind of attention you get by standing up in front of thousands of people."

"You are a lucky man."

"Yes, I am. We all are. We somehow were in the right place at the right time. Somehow things clicked. We were successful enough that we didn't have to get a real job. We could go on doing what we love doing. To regret any of it would be foolish. Leaving Pink Floyd was a bit like driving away from a dodgy wedding with cans dragging behind the car rattling all the time. There was a lot of enmity. I've left it behind me."

We talked a little longer about Live 8 and the artists he'd seen and met during the day. When we were done, I turned the interview into a more informal conversation and, with a plan in mind, asked Roger about the recent release of Nick's autobiography.

"What did you think of Inside Out?"

"He showed me the original draft. A lot of was written during the bad years when I was the big ogre. He asked for my comments, so I went through it and almost the entire thing was blue pencil. He changed odd little bits. He writes the most marvellous fiction. People unwittingly construct memories that are convenient and favourable to the ego. It may well be that I can, for instance, remember sitting in the shed at the bottom of my garden in London and putting together the quarter-inch tape with all the cash register sounds for the beginning of Money on my own. He remembers us doing it together. Maybe he was there. It's possible. Who knows?"

I then dropped the question I was so desperately longing to ask.

"Remember the book you wanted me to write all those years ago?"

"Hm, not sure I do, Matt."

"Your management sent me a letter on your behalf asking me not to proceed."

"They did? Must have been in my ogre years," Roger said, laughing.

"Would you mind me finishing it? I know David's cool with it, and I hope you are, too. I just want to keep the Live 8 momentum going and finish it while everybody is still on a high."

"OK, no problem. I know I can trust you to write an

unbiased story. And to get all the facts right. I can, can't I?"

"Of course, you can."

"Then go for it, Matt. Need anything from me?"

"Actually, I would like to sit down and do one more interview and go through some topics we've never touched on over the years."

"Topics like what?" Roger asked, faking a worried frown.

"Morality, ethics, and politics," I replied laughing.

"Don't know fuck about politics. You know I'm a man without an opinion," he guffawed. "Just arrange it with management. I'll prepare them for it."

▪ ▪ ▪

They'd planned the session with David Gilmour for the next day. Same hotel, same suite. David was in a good mood, but still his modest, quiet self. It was nice to see him again, but hard figuring out whether he was looking forward to doing the interview. I presumed not, so I kept the pleasantries to a minimum.

"David, what made you finally commit to Live 8 although you initially had strong reservations about it?"

"Like most people, I wanted to do everything in my power to encourage the leaders of the G8 to really do something about poverty in the world. True, I had some reservations about it. When Bob rang and asked if I would do Live 8 with Pink Floyd, he didn't mention Roger. He just said: 'Will you put Pink Floyd back together to do Live 8?' I said, 'No. I'm in the middle of my solo album.' But then he came down to see me, despite me telling him not to, and explained the whole thing. That made me feel a bit guilty, but at first I hung on to my selfishness. But he really wanted us to take part."

"What changed your mind?"

"Raising funds to relieve poverty in Africa is, obviously, a noble cause to work for, and it was great to be a part of that. But you know, all the bitterness and rubbish that's been going on for the last twenty-odd years... It's nice to box that all up so you can forget about it. My youngest kids have never really see me do all that Pink Floyd stuff, and that's a shame. So they were part of the equation, too. They were there, right down in front of the stage, waving and shouting. They loved it. My kids now understand that I'm not just this bum who lazes around the house, cooks them dinner and takes them to school."

"Many people are wondering if you'll do it, again. If there's any possibility a tour."

"It was great to be on the stage with Nick, Rick and Roger again. Hatred and bitterness are terribly negative things. It felt incredibly good to put all that into perspective. I believe we've now rounded it off nicely. It's a powerful thing, this old Pink Floyd business, but I have no great desire to do it again. Perhaps if the right moment came up at some point to do another one-off thing, I don't think I'd look on it too harshly. That said, I do not intend to go out on tour with Pink Floyd again."

"How was it working with Roger, after all that has been said in the past?"

"The first meeting was pretty stilted and cagey, to be honest. The songs Roger wanted to do were not the ones I thought we should do. Roger wanted to do Another Brick In The Wall, but I didn't think it was appropriate. This was a thing for Africa, and I didn't think that little children in Africa should sing 'We don't need no education.' There was no discussion on that one. I was totally right. The rehearsals convinced me that working with Roger wasn't something I wanted to be doing a lot of. Live 8 was great, but it was closure. Roger and I still talk, and it's better than it has been. But it wouldn't work. People change and Roger and I have outgrown each other. There's no realistic basis for us to work together. Pink Floyd has no future."

"What's up for you next, then?"

"I don't want to use the word dilettante, but I'm not dominated by music every second of every day, which I was in my twenties and thirties. There are the children, Polly is writing, we are a family where different things have to be prioritised at different times. I can no longer relate to the dedication and religious fervour of our youth. But something's lost and something's gained in living every day, as Joni Mitchell would say. I am in some ways wiser, more knowledgeable, and better at doing things. So hopefully all that goes into the music."

"I somehow can't picture you stopping recording or performing."

"I want people to listen to the music that I make. I want them to experience at least a tenth of the pleasure I get from making music and putting an album together. There are moments when you make a record and you come across some notes or a piece of music floats in out of the air, you think: 'That's so fucking brilliant!' And you give thanks to whatever higher being guided it towards you. I want to feel that the public, all those other people in the world, get a bit of that emotion when they listen to the music that I make. My children are obsessed with music in the way I was when I was their age. Sometimes I think I'm jaded, that nothing can turn me on anymore. And then I see Leonard Cohen, and go 'No, by Christ, I'm still capable of being moved.'"

Although we continued to talk and I asked a couple more questions, I wasn't really listening anymore. My mind had got stuck on his firm statement that there was no future for Pink Floyd. By the sound of it, that included a Pink Floyd without Roger Waters. I was disappointed and sad. Geldof and Live 8 had brought the firm back together, not to give us hope, but to put an end to all hope and speculation. A last farewell. Thank you and goodnight.

At the end of the interview, I wished David good luck with the upcoming release of his new solo album, which, I'd learned, was planned for release early next year. I said I hoped we'd meet each other again after the release. He thanked me and said he'd look forward to it. I didn't mention the book as I had to Roger, yesterday.

As of today, the story had taken on a new perspective.

58

WEARING THE INSIDE OUT

Fort William, Scottish Highlands, September 16, 2008

I sat down on a log, unsure if it was driftwood or left there on purpose. The small pebbled beach gave me a superb view over the large lake or loch, as they call it here in Scotland. With almost no wind, the water was like a huge black slate of glass, ringed by green hills and forests. Up in the air, three birds of prey soared high on the late summer thermals. All was quiet. Blissfully quiet.

The loch was only a few steps away from our rented cabin home. Anna and I desperately needed some downtime and the rural surroundings of the peaceful, unspoiled area were the main reason we'd picked this spot. The lodge, which was situated close to the little town of Fort William, seemed like the perfect place to take a breather, both physically and mentally. To put things in perspective.

We both led busy lives and had somehow become all tangled up in the emotional chaos that surrounded our little family and individual careers. As we were both nearly sixty, we felt it was time for us to take a short break. Anna's father had passed quietly away in his sleep three months ago; he was 87. Anna had been close to her father and needed to look after her mother. She had given up her summer holidays to stay in her old family home for a month.

Anna's mother had Alzheimer's and really needed to move. As a result, supporting her mum and finding a suitable home for her, Anna had also had to put the current home on the market. I'd started a small online company six years ago, mainly building websites and providing e-commerce services, that sort of thing. But we were doing very well and I couldn't just abandon, so we decided I would stay at home.

While Anna was away, I got a call from Sport's brother informing me that my old buddy had died. Cancer. Sport had known he was ill but had chosen not to tell friends or family. Without warning or a chance to say goodbye, my pal was gone. It hit me like a brick, and I didn't know whether I should feel angry or sad.

To make matters worse, two days later, I received an email from a friend saying that Carly had committed suicide. She'd overdosed on XTC and cocaine. We'd lost contact many years ago, but she was the first girl I'd ever really cared about. It brought a load of memories rushing back. Mostly, though, I was stunned to learn that, of all people, she'd been battling with a drug problem. The Carly I'd known had been a sweet, sensitive little butterfly, curiously fluttering through life without a care in the world. Sure, she dumped me after we'd briefly lived together. But in retrospect, I couldn't really blame her: I probably wasn't the nicest person to live with at the time. Wondering why and how Carly's life had taken such a wrong turn, I couldn't help feeling gutted, confused and alone.

I found the death of friends and loved ones extremely hard to deal with. It just wasn't fair. Anne said it probably reminded me of my mortality, and she was probably right. It didn't make me feel any better, though. I bent over, picked up a handful of pebbles from the beach and, one by one, let them slip through my fingers.

Renting the cabin had seemed like a good idea. The fresh air would do us both good. Or so we thought. News of Rick Wright's passing broke the news yesterday. Another colossal blow to the stomach. And this one that made me cry.

Two years ago, Syd had died. I'd only met him once and knew he wasn't doing well. The media was full of stories about Syd's days with Pink Floyd, quoting band members and friends from the sixties. I remember Nick Mason saying in Time Magazine that Syd was "the nucleus that created Pink Floyd". I'd thought that was a nice way of putting it. Nick had also said that without Syd's initial influence, the odds were that none of them would have found their way into the music business and that Pink Floyd in any form would simply not have existed. I think he was right.

While Syd's passing was sad and surrounded by sentiment, to me the news of Richard's death hit me ten times harder. Even though he and I were never close, I admired him for being such a sensitive soul and for staying true to himself when the going got tough. Life in Pink Floyd must not have been easy with alpha males like Roger and David around. The times Rick and I spent together had meant a lot to me. Once I'd earned his trust, we'd sit and have long, meaningful conversations about all kinds of things, not just music. I cherished those moments. He never expressed his own feelings much, but Rick was the only band member who ever showed any sincere interest in my life. Not as a friend, but simply because he was a gentle human being and had a genuine interest in other people.

Rick's importance to the Floyd sound was often overlooked. His monumental harmonic progressions were key to the success of Dark Side Of The Moon and Wish You Were Here. Rick tied the sound together; with Us And Them and The Great Gig In The Sky as his two classic masterpieces.

Sitting looking out over the lake, some conversations we'd had played back in my head. I remembered meeting him for the first time in Amsterdam, talking to him that day at Charlton Park and our phone call, shortly after he was fired. It had only been brief, but I was glad and grateful we met one more time at the reunion at Live 8, three years ago.

No successful rock musician is a saint, and neither was Richard. There were rumours about drug abuse, which I found hard to believe. I wasn't sure if he was a faithful husband, though. Wearing a ring meant little in rock 'n' roll. Especially in the seventies with all the fame, glory and money that came with early success. I'd seen more than enough evidence of that, walking around backstage and in the early morning hotel lobbies when I was with them on the road.

I felt sorry for his children. James, Gala, and Ben had lost their father. The idea of not being able to see Elisa growing up and having kids of her own, suddenly frightened me.

"Everything OK, dear?" Anna sat down next to me.

"Yeah, I just feel sad about Rick Wright. Can't believe he's gone. He's left us some monumental music. I wonder what my legacy will be?"

"How's that?" Anna asked.

"The news of his death has really affected me, like I've just lost a relative or someone real close. I wonder why that is? The more I think about it, the more I believe it's because of what he has meant for me. I grew up with Pink Floyd's music. His music. It is the soundtrack to my life. Rick Wright touched the souls of millions of people. Including mine. That is his legacy. What will I leave the world when I die? It all feels so insignificant compared to the great artists, writers, poets and politicians of the world."

"You're very important to Elisa and me..."

"That's sweet of you to say," I replied, "but when the three of us are no longer around, I don't think many people will remember us. In, say, a hundred years' time, people will still listen to the music of Pink Floyd as we still listen to Bach and Beethoven. They've made an everlasting impact on art and history."

"Why is leaving a mark so important to you?" Anna asked, putting an arm around my shoulders.

"That's difficult to explain," I said after a few seconds of thought. "I guess I'm trying to put my existence into perspective. Why am I here? Does it make any sense? Do I make any sense on this overcrowded planet? Is there anything left for me to do that means something to somebody before I'm gone? I honestly don't know."

"Think of all the people you've met along the way, and the people you still speak to and see; the ones that care about you. I am one thousand percent sure that you've enriched a lot of lives just by being who you are. Isn't that all that matters?"

"I hope so. I don't understand why finding these answers is so important to me."

"Maybe there are no answers to these questions? Maybe there is no real meaning to life..."

"That's perhaps the scariest realisation of all. That we are here for no reason. That our planet is doomed as soon as the sun stops shining. That everything we ever did, the complete history of humanity, was all in vain. You know what my first thoughts were when Elisa was born?"

"No, you've never told me."

"The first thing that crossed my mind was that I could not die. That you and I had to stay alive to protect her from all the lies and bullshit in this world, to be her first and last line of defence. That's weird, isn't it? Your baby is born and the first thing you think of is how not to die. And now that death rears its ugly head all around us, I am reminded of the promise I made that day. I see all my own lines of defence fall. Who's protecting me? What path should I walk when the people I care about are no longer around? How can I safeguard Elisa when I no longer feel safe myself?"

"You're in a dark place, sweetie. We came here to lighten up."

"Yeah, I know. Sorry about that. Let's blame Mr Wright for that. I don't care if there never will be another Pink Floyd album. Still, it feels like a definite closure. The end of an era. That too, makes me feel sentimental."

"Let's go inside and open up a bottle. There's a stew in the oven. As meaningless as it may seem for you now, there's plenty in life to look forward to."

"You're right, Anna. Let's raise a glass in remembrance of Richard. To us and him."

61

OUTSIDE THE WALL

The Ship, Rotherhithe, London, May 12, 2011

I'd finally found time to call Kevin on my mobile last night. He shared my love of all things Floyd and I'd been dying to talk to him ever since I'd seen Waters' production of The Wall at the Gelredome in the Netherlands, a couple of weeks back. It was 21 years since I'd been to his live performance of the album in Berlin, and when Waters announced he was kicking off a new European tour, I persuaded myself to buy a ticket and travelled to the beautiful city of Arnhem. Who knew if I'd ever get another chance to see the Wall played live? Any reservations I had about the gig were blown clear away the moment the lights went out. Waters put on a spectacular show. From the cheers and rapturous applause, the 30.000-capacity audience loved it, too. I only found out later that Roger created quite a controversy in Holland when he produced an imitation machine gun and pointed it at the audience which, by the way, was a normal part of the show. Sadly, however, a crazed gunman had killed six people by opening fire using a machine gun in a Dutch mall, only two days before the concert. Apparently some local media were not impressed, calling Roger 'shameful' and 'insensitive'. It was not known if Roger was aware of the tragedy prior to the show, though.

“You know he’s going to join Roger Waters, right?” Kevin suddenly said.

“Who is?”

“David Gilmour.”

“You’re joking, right?”

“No, I’m not. Tonight. At the 02 Arena. Got it from a reliable source at Live Nation.”

“Wow! Any chance you can get us in?”

“Don’t know. Let me see if I can pull a few strings...”

“Would you mind if I ask Derek along?”

“No, not at all. It would be fun to see him again. I’ll call you as soon as I have some good news.”

▪ ▪ ▪

Kevin was manager of a catering company that did gigs for Live Nation, and a while later he phoned back to say he’d got us premium tickets, no less. I messaged Derek the good news, and we agreed that we’d all meet at the O2.

Derek was a former high school teacher who’d switched careers to run a successful online design business. We’d met at a web publishing conference, and I quickly became one of his clients. He had an expert eye for detail, knew everything about online design, and never missed a deadline. After I introduced him to Kevin, he built a great website for his company. When it turned out we also shared musical preferences, we all became friends.

Seeing Roger perform his jaw-dropping Wall-extravaganza twice in one month was incredible. Somehow I could take in more of all that was happening: the sound effects, the pyrotechnics, the lights and stunning visuals. This was the first time Kevin and Derek had seen The Wall live and they were even more impressed than I was. The mind-boggling scale of it alone had blown them away. The stage where the wall was erected was vast, expanding right out to either side of the venue, and everything from the enormous high-definition 200 by 50-foot projections to Gerald Scarfe's puppets and animations seemed larger than life. And so were Roger's political messages. Together with the 3D sonic effects and clean, crisp sound, it was a dynamic, overpowering feast for the senses.

When it was all over, the remnants of the euphoria we had felt enfolded us into the night, past the merch table and back onto the street outside. We needed a drink and headed straight for our favourite watering hole, which was only a few stops away. The Ship was a smashing little pub. They treated us to a warm and friendly welcome: a pint of Irish red ale for Kevin, cider for Derek and apple juice for me, which for once raised no wisecracks, and took ourselves over to a table.

There seemed to be only one thing we unanimously had serious reservations about: the music had sounded just a little too good.

"Are you sure everything was played live?" Derek asked. They both looked at me inquiringly.

"Hard to tell these days," I replied. "It wouldn't surprise me if parts of it were pre-recorded."

"What makes you think that?" Derek queried.

"Well, and I got this from somebody close to the band, rumour is that during Roger's Pros And Cons tour everything except the vocals and Clapton's guitar was played from tape. If it's true, I don't know, but it wouldn't surprise me. I remember being at one of those gigs and thinking 'Wow, this is the best live sound I've ever heard.' Which was peculiar since I knew the venue for its bad acoustics and reverberations. I know some people have uploaded clips to YouTube revealing Waters lip synching during his Dark Side

Of The Moon solo tour."

"But would it change our opinion on how good tonight's show was if we knew he was cheating?" Kevin asked.

"It would for me," Derek said. "I like music to be real. I wouldn't mind if he sang a few false notes or missed a beat on his bass. As long as it's real."

"I had a great night no matter what," Kevin countered.

"We'll never know, will we?" I concluded. "One thing I know for certain, Gilmour's solo was as real as it gets."

"Yeah, man," Kevin agreed. "It gave me goosebumps. Shivers down my spine."

Derek nodded.

Being of the privileged few who knew what the night might have in store, our expectations were on a constant high. We had no idea whether David really would make an appearance. For all we knew, it could have been a big hoax. But then, just after the interval as he was singing Comfortably Numb, Waters pointed upwards and, out of nowhere, Gilmour appeared on top of the wall. The crowd were on their feet, roaring with delight as David played his parts with flawless flair and ferocity. I saw people crying and even I had a bit of a lump in my throat. After the closing songs, Roger brought David back on the stage, thanking him for the "enormous honour" and then to everyone's utter amazement Nick Mason joined them onstage. It had been a sight to behold: David on mandolin, Roger on trumpet, and Nick playing tambourine with a backing band that included good old Snowy White. They did an unplugged version of Outside The Wall and then Roger directly addressed the audience: "When we first played this more than thirty years ago, I was a grumpy fellow disaffected with rock and playing live, as David will attest. But all that has changed."

"Could this be a first step towards reconciliation and

possibly a new Pink Floyd record? Or tour?" Derek pondered sipping at his cider.

"Don't think so," I replied. "Can't see that happening. Putting them back together in a studio would kick off the whole ego battle about who writes what, who gets the credits and who has the final say in the creative process, all over again. David has said he never wants to do extensive tours again. An it wouldn't be right to go on a tour without Rick Wright anyhow."

"Guess, you're right," Derek said. "Still a damn shame."

"It was a sympathetic gesture on Roger's part," Kevin added, "to acknowledge that David and Nick were part of The Wall."

"Agreed," I said.

"Pretty stupid of him to sue his former mates over the band name, though," Derek noted.

"Yeah, he was wrong to do that. It closed a lot of doors. I never thought we'd see them back on stage again. It makes tonight extra special."

"With age comes wisdom," Kevin concluded.

"Arguments or not, they did a lot of great work together. It's true when they say the whole Floyd is greater than the sum of its parts. Their music wouldn't have existed if any of them hadn't been there."

"Do you have a favourite Pink Floyd album, Matt?" Kevin asked.

"It chops and changes. I like the dynamics, musical contrasts, rough edges and sense of anger on The Wall. Obviously, Dark Side Of The Moon and Wish You Were Here feature some great, classic tunes, but I've heard those just a little too often for comfort. Recently, I've found myself more drawn to Meddle and Animals. It depends on the mood I'm in. And you?"

"Still go for Dark Side Of The Moon. Their finest hour."

"I'm much more into their early stuff," Derek advanced, not to be left out. "The first two albums are fuckin' brilliant."

"I remember Nick once saying that they got paid two hundred and fifty quid for their early gigs.

And that was only after they played their first hit on the radio." I rejoined.

"Hit?" Kevin asked.

"Two, as a matter of fact. Arnold Layne and See Emily Play. Both in 1967 and both thanks to Syd Barrett."

"He's grown into this mythical figure," Derek forwarded, attempting an analysis, "I've never quite understood it," he continued, "Sure, he wrote some great, ground-breaking music, but that was only for a short period. Pink Floyd didn't become famous until long after Barrett was gone."

"They had a bit of a rough start," I explained, slightly on the defensive. "They weren't very popular outside London at first. People would pour beer over them and chuck stuff. Fortunately, they had a decent following on mainland Europe by this time and did some extensive touring over there. When Syd started to seriously unravel they could easily have called it quits right then. But they didn't."

We ordered another round and our little post-concert conference continued.

"Any idea what induced them to carry on despite the odds?" Kevin probed me.

"The Floyd started out as a R&B group and were really not that good. Rick was the only properly schooled musician among them. When drugs got involved, even he let go of the notion they had to play 3-minute songs. They quit worrying about chords and compact song structures and maxed the volume of their guitars. When David Gilmour joined the band there were suddenly two skilled musicians on board. That the door opened to play real songs with choruses and nice chord progressions again. The improvisation and sonic experiments carried on for a while, but a lot of that was the band covering for a lack of purpose and musical direction after Syd left."

Kevin and Derek listened attentively as if I was some kind of lecturer, their glasses down at their side. I went on.

"They toured a lot with other bands and surrounded themselves with top class studio people until, slowly but surely, they had the experience and the confidence to come up with some decent songs without Barrett's help. After some trial and error and a couple of mediocre records - Ummagumma and Atom Heart Mother are my least favourite Floyd LP's - they released Meddle. From then on, things changed. Roger had found his voice as lyricist by now and was suddenly touching on universal themes a lot of people could relate to. The band was never out of the Abbey Road, later Britannia Row Studios where they spent all their time pushing the boundaries of the world-class recording equipment at their disposal. Roger gets peeved at any suggestion he and Nick were more into the sound effects, and David and Rick were the real musicians. And he's actually right: they all liked to muck around with sound, using a wind machine to make the links between songs, stuff like that. In the meantime, the stereo market exploded in size, especially among the college-age consumers, and better gear became available at lower prices. Back then, people would get together in each others living rooms and play their favourite albums front to back. A little gentle bragging about the audio set-up in your living room was almost obligatory. Pink Floyd provided the ultimate soundtrack for that. When Dark Side Of The Moon came out, there was no turning back. Money finally came flowing in by the buckets and the rest is history. But, hey, that's just my little Pink-Floyd-in-a-nutshell-theory."

"You should write a book about the band," Kevin joked,

fully aware of my rollercoaster experience with the touchy subject. And my lack of determination in following up, probably too.

"Fuck you, Kev!" I laughed. "You wait, I'll sell the rights to Steven Spielberg. No tickets for you when I get invited to the Academy Awards."

"You'll have to finish it first, Mr Blockbuster. I haven't seen a single page, so far."

"I'm working on it, guys. Taking my time in true Pink Floyd fashion," I said jesting, although, in all honesty, I wasn't having much luck getting myself motivated again. I felt guilty about not finishing the book; somehow I had to get the writing rebooted.

Fortunately, Derek switched the subject back to the band. "Looking at all the things that went wrong after they made it big, what do you think was the core problem? Was Roger Waters really the root of all the evil?"

"I think it's much more complicated than that. They were a band with four quite different and complex personalities. At first, their shared quest for fame and fortune bound them together. The success of the band took priority over individual success. Once they'd reached that common goal, the sense of urgency was gone and they started to question the band's musical direction and each other's commitment. Or lack of commitment, really."

"They lost respect for each other?" Derek suggested.

"I think so, yes."

"Success and ego, a lethal combination," Kevin noted.

"Money, it's a gas..." Derek laughed. "It was Roger who screwed things up by leaving."

"Again," I said, "it's not that simple. Roger came up with most of the songs and he wrote all of the lyrics. When he left in 1985, he thought the band was finished creatively and assumed that, without him, it would fold. He underestimated David's determination not to give up, as well as his resourcefulness in finding the right people to create new Floyd music. That they could put aside their differences and come together for Live 8 did them all a lot of good. Pink Floyd had nothing left to prove. Except perhaps that it took all four of them to create the unique Floyd sound we're familiar with."

"Still no plans for a reunion, though..." Kevin sighed.

"It would never work," I said. "Why should they? They don't need the money. David and Roger were in their thirties when Roger left the group. They're well into their sixties now and have a total watch over their own interests and aspirations. I doubt if they have anything left in common."

"Any ideas on forward moves? Retirement?" Derek asked.

"I can see them doing more solo work. If Roger can take Dark Side Of The Moon and The Wall on tour, why can't he do the other Pink Floyd albums, as well? Nick could well pop up every now and again, supporting his old band mates. As long as they're physically capable of doing it, I see no reason why they would retire."

"And the book gets thicker and thicker..." Kevin deadpanned.

"OK, lads, time to call it a day," I said smiling. "It's getting late and I've got a full day of writing ahead of me."

67
ABSOLUTELY CURTAINS

Berkeley Hotel, London, July 5, 2017

"I'm here to see Rachel. She's with Sony Records."

"I believe she's sitting right over there," the desk servant said, pointing at a brunette sitting in a corner of the hotel lobby with a stack of papers on her lap.

After the Live 8 video sessions in 2005, I'd never received a reply to my request for an interview. Either Roger had forgotten to let his management team know we had a deal or, in spite of his promise, Roger had no genuine desire for another meeting.

A couple more tries and several messages later, I simply gave up. Without one last interview, I just couldn't think of a suitable ending to the story. Maybe this book was never meant to be. With the passing of Richard Wright and the release of The Endless River, all hope of a new chapter in Pink Floyd's history was gone, anyway. I felt it was time to let the band go.

That was until in June 2017 the release of Roger's fourth solo album, Is This the Life We Really Want?, opened a window of opportunity for one last try. Miraculously, it worked. With a promise that I'd include his latest, quite brilliant effort in the book, I managed to set up an exclusive two-hour interview at London's The Berkeley Hotel.

"Rachel?"

"You must be Matt," Rachel said. She stood up and shook my hand. "Nice to meet you. Roger's expecting you. Come, I'll show you to his room."

The Berkeley, a stylish 5-star luxury hang-out for the rich and famous, had all the majestic grandeur befitting a 100-year-old hotel. A perfect place for two gentlemen of now some considerable age.

Rachel led me up a flight of stairs and through some swanky hallways to one of the suites on the first floor. "You're a privileged man," she said, without turning her head.

"Why's that?" I asked.

"Most journalists get 20 minutes. Max."

I smiled to myself but said nothing.

Rachel stopped in front of room 104. "I've arranged for some coffee and tea. If you need anything else, I'll be right outside. I'll give you a ten minutes heads-up when the two hours are up, OK?"

"Sounds great. Thanks, Rachel."

She knocked and opened the door without waiting.

The familiar tall figure of Roger Waters was standing in the middle of the room, his hand outstretched. "Sir Matt! Long time no see!"

We kicked off with some pleasant catch-up chit chat, mainly about our kids and the wives. Roger said he was enjoying living in New York these days.

"As you probably know, I moved to the US because my youngest kid was there. And then I sort of stayed. You can walk to a lot of places in New York. I've recently taken to using the subway a lot, because it's much faster than going anywhere in a car or in a taxi. I like it on the subway. I often travel in the middle of the day. It's nice to sit and look at the other people travelling. You see who lives in this city and how diverse and cosmopolitan it is."

"Don't you miss anything about England?" I asked, jumpstarting my last-chapter-of-the-book interview session.

"I miss a sense of decency and fair play. It still exists, but it's become hidden. There's a quote outside the Lords cricket grounds: 'It matters not who won or lost, but how you play the game.' I thought it was quintessentially English, but it was written by an American!"

"And as uncle Bob said: 'times they are a changin'."

"They are. And fast! I feel enormously privileged to have been born in 1943 and not 1983. To have been around when there was a music business and the takeover by Silicon Valley hadn't happened. You could still make a living writing and recording songs and playing them to people."

Somehow it sounded a bit odd, coming from a man who was recently named number 10 on the Sunday Times list of richest musicians with an estimated fortune of 160 million pounds.

"This gallery of rogues and thieves," Roger continued, "has injected themselves between the people who aspire to be creative and their potential audience. They steal every fucking cent anybody ever made and put it in their pockets to buy huge mega-yachts and Gulfstream Fives. It's just stealing. And that they're allowed to get away with it is incredible."

"You sound angry," I ventured, looking appropriately serious.

"I am angry, even though it doesn't change my life in any way. I blame the punters as well, to some extent. There's an entire generation that believes music should be free. I mean, why not make everything free? Then you could walk into a shop and say, 'I like that television' and you walk out with it.

No. Somebody made that, and you must buy it!"

"The rules of the game have changed," I put in.

"True. Fortunately, my mother always told me there are good people everywhere in the world. And she's right. I inherited my believe in humanity from my father's sacrifice and my mother's convictions. I'm going out on tour again this summer, putting on a whole new show. It's a wake-up call. It's saying, 'This is not a drill. The huge corporate machine is killing you.'"

"You've been raising your political voice a lot more over the last few years."

"I used to go to political meetings with my mother when I was six and my brother was eight. My mother was a card-carrying member of the Communist party until I was 13. She left the party in '56, as most of them did. So, I have quite vivid memories of that and have been aware of politics from a young age. In fact, I met my first wife under a trestle table at a Daily Worker bazaar when we were about six years old. Cambridge University has always been a hotbed of Bolshevism."

Roger smiled. I laughed, too.

"You know, Matt," Roger continued, "I've grown up considerably. I might sound angry at times, but I've become less angry about other people's frailties. When I'm being super-critical, often what irritates me is really saying something about me. I project my inadequacies onto others. I used to do it hugely in the past. I've gotten a lot better. I feel much more secure than when I, um, wrote The Wall."

"You seem a lot more at peace now than, say, 25 years ago," I offered.

"Thanks. I think I'm operating from a more adult place than I've ever done. You know, the abandoned child component of my personality remained powerful throughout most of my adult life. It's only through some recent events that I've come to understand that and begun to consciously deal with it. I am 73 years old and it's never too late to grow up. Considering everything that's going on in the world, though, I'm still searching for answers to questions that are unanswerable. The one thing that I am optimistic about is the explosion of information technology. We now at least have a better chance to at least pose these questions for ourselves."

"They have accused you of being anti-Semitic. That must have caused a lot of pain..."

"Look, I remember my mother's friends after the war. I remember Maria and Claudette. I remember their tattoos. They were two of the lucky ones to survive. My mother said our house was full of evidence of the heinous, ghastly crimes committed in the name of the appalling ideology of national socialism and the Third Reich. For a kid living in England, I was as close to the experience as you could get. I saw the aftermath of it. My mother spent the rest of her life devoting herself entirely to political activities that she believed would bring the greater good to the greater number of people, and that was what she did. And my father, as you know, died fighting the Nazis in southern Italy."

"I know, but that doesn't explain why you are so engaged in the Israeli-Palestine dispute."

"I have no choice but to do what I do, Matt. My political life and my feeling that I must take part and be active is absolutely dictated by the example of both my parents. I've been involved in BDS, the Palestinian-led Boycott, Divestment, Sanctions movement for about 15 years now. When somebody criticises the Israeli government, if they call them an anti-Semite loudly enough and long enough, it may just divert people away from the fact that the person they're calling an anti-Semite is almost certainly an advocate of basic human rights for all our brothers and sisters all over the world irrespective of their religion, or colour, or nationality, or anything else."

Roger Waters took a deep breath and continued.

"You either recognise others as being as important as you are or the same as you are. I often like to transcend it by generation: Is your child as important as my child? Because as parents, we have feelings for our children. If you conclude that the answer is 'yes', then you have an absolute duty and responsibility to act as a collective part. In the spirit of the beehive: we're all in this together. I'm just a bee, but I have an absolute responsibility to make sure that the queen isn't a fucking asshole who's going to destroy us all. We all look after one another as best we can."

I hesitated for a second. In preparing for the interview, I'd saved the political questions for last, but here we were steering headlong into them. And I felt Roger was dodging the question by saying he has no choice. Of course, he has a choice. Everyone does.

"You've obviously chosen the side of the Palestinians and that pisses off the Israeli's, including your fans from Israel. You could have chosen to stay neutral."

Roger's reacted like he'd been hit by a truck. Sitting up, he looked me straight in the eye and raised his voice.

"The Palestinian people are struggling for their basic human rights. In 1948, the United Nations drafted and subsequently adopted a Universal Declaration of Human Rights which enshrined in international law that all our brothers and sisters all over the world, irrespective of their ethnicity or nationality or religion, have certain basic human rights including but not limited to, the right to life and self-determination. So, the question you should ask me, is: do I agree with that United Nations Declaration?"

"You obviously do."

"Yes, you're damn right I do. But now a second question arises: am I prepared to stand behind my support for human rights and act upon it? Will I help my brothers and sisters in their struggle for human rights or will I cross over and walk by on the other side? The people of Palestine live under a deeply repressive apartheid regime of occupation and enjoy neither the right to life nor the right to self-determination. Back in 2004, Palestinian Civil Society appealed to the rest of the world for help and established a cultural picket line, asking artists not to perform in Israel until the Israeli government recognises the right of Palestinians to life and self-determination. Since that time, I have responded to their call and done what I can to persuade others to do the same."

He paused for a moment.

"Some of my fellow musicians recently performed in Israel. They say they are doing it to build bridges and further the cause of peace. Bullshit! To perform in Israel is a lucrative gig, but to do so serves to normalise the occupation, the apartheid, the ethnic cleansing, the incarceration of children, the routine slaughter of unarmed protesters, and so on. Because I support human rights and criticise the Israeli government for its violations, I am accused of being anti-Semitic. I should point out that I support the fight for human rights for all oppressed peoples everywhere. The religion of the oppressor is neither here nor there. If I support the Rohingyas and deplore the Myanmar persecution of them, it doesn't make me anti-Buddhist. There's only one race, and it's the human race, and we all belong to it."

"Even the richest countries in the world, including the one you now live in, have their fair share of poverty."

"I'm doing alright. I make a ton of money. I'm fine. But most people live on the breadline. And not just the homeless bums on the streets. Everybody is under pressure. Why? It's written into corporate law. The people who run everything have literally only one responsibility: maximise the returns of their shareholders. That's it. They have no social responsibility and no responsibility to their workers, which you think would be obvious to all those out-of-work coal miners in West Virginia, who are dying, mostly of diabetes, because all they can afford is shit food and because nobody's told them that there's a better life."

"The American dream..."

"They've been told to pull themselves up by their bootstraps, and if they work hard, they can be Jeff Bezos. No, you can't, guys. It's the lie they have fed you all your fucking lives. Like the lie that America is great and is spreading good all over the world, and if only everybody subscribed to the same values they expect you to live under, everything would be fine. No, it wouldn't. It's a desperately rotten system, and it's causing untold misery. Will it ever get addressed? I have no idea. I won't see it in my lifetime, but I hope they don't destroy the planet before a generation of younger people come along."

"I understand what you're saying," I replied, "but why don't you let people decide for themselves? To quote Alice Cooper: 'When musicians are telling people what to do or who to vote for, isn't that an abuse of power? You're telling your fans not to think for themselves, just to think like you. Rock 'n' roll is about freedom and that's not freedom.'"

And then, quite unintentionally, I dropped a bombshell.

"You played Moscow, although the Russians violated the borders of Ukraine. You played in the USA although they invaded Syria, Libya, and Iraq. Isn't that a little hypocritical? And if I'm not mistaken, you played in Israel, as well, during the Dark Side Of The Moon tour in 2006. I think..."

"Actually, Matt, I don't give a fuck what you think."

His words reverberated through the old Victorian hotel room like gunshots in a cathedral. The look in his eyes was the coldest I had ever seen.

Stunned and unable to comprehend what had just happened, I desperately tried to think of a suitable retort. I'd been hurt by a long-time friend and he obviously didn't care. Admittedly, we'd had our share of disagreements over the past fifty years, but they'd always been quickly dispelled with a handshake or a joke. Not today. Today was different.

Had I been too blunt in my observations? Had I underestimated how sensitive the issue was? I had no idea. I took a few deep breaths and as my confusion slowly faded, anger took over.

"Well, I think you're an ass, too!" I heard myself blurt out.

Instantly, Roger Waters' face softened and with a curious mix of affection and pity, he slowly raised himself up out of the chair and walked towards the door. As he passed behind me, I felt him pat my shoulder with his hand, exactly as he'd done fifty years ago on the day we first met.

"I think 'pain in the ass' is the expression you're looking for," Waters said as he left the room. "A pain in the ass. And proud of it!"

Still sitting in my chair, I turned my head and looked into the hallway where Roger was talking to Rachel. I couldn't hear what he was saying, but he still looked agitated. Rachel mostly seemed surprised. A little later, I saw her handing him a pen and a sheet of paper. Roger then leaned over a piece of hotel furniture, wrote something down and, folding the paper, handed it back to Rachel. Then he just walked off.

I saw Rachel walking over to me. I stood up.

"I don't know exactly what just happened," she lied, "but Roger is clearly upset and excused himself. He asked me to give you this."

She handed me the note. "I've got to head back to the lobby and wait for the journalists to arrive. Sorry your chat didn't work out as planned."

When she'd gone, I looked at the paper in my hand. After a few indecisive seconds I unfolded the note to read the words Roger had written down:

If you are neutral in situations of injustice, you have chosen the side of the oppressor.

Desmond Tutu

67

THEIR MORTAL REMAINS

Victoria & Albert Museum, London, August 5th, 2017

It was a long walk from South Kensington's underground station to the Victoria & Albert museum. In my street-level memories of previous visits, it was just a few minutes away. Now I took me at least ten. Ten minutes of contemplation. I'd had no idea when I'd booked the ticket online, but today, it just felt too good to be true. This was more than a simple coincidence, it had to be fate. This day was meant to be.

When I woke up this morning and checked my updates, my Facebook timeline was saying that on this very day, exactly fifty years ago, Piper At The Gates Of Dawn had been released. On this day of all days, I have a ticket to go see Their Mortal Remains, the exhibition celebrating the legacy of Pink Floyd. Who would have believed Piper At The Gates Of Dawn would mark the beginning of such an illustrious career? That this unlikely bunch of guys from Cambridge were on the verge of becoming an internationally famous recording and performing act? That the early psychedelic Pink Floyd would set a standard that bands all over the world attempt to follow? And that fifty years on, hundreds of thousands of people would visit their career-spanning exhibition in the Victoria & Albert Museum? Not me. No way!

I almost missed the small underground exit to the museum. Luckily, I spotted two young kids in Pink Floyd t-shirts. When they took an unexpected right, I followed. Hundreds of stone, bronze, and marble statues on both sides of the hallway accompanied me to the temporary exhibition entrance and with my pre-booked ticket in hand, I had no trouble in finding the right queue. Ten minutes later, I got a headset and was pointed to the first of many rooms.

▪ ▪ ▪

The familiar Meddle 'ping' marked the start of the audio tour. Suddenly, I was standing eye to eye with an oversized model of a black Bedford, a similar van to the Ford Transit I'd seen many, many years ago in Amsterdam. A framed picture of the van showed Nick loading some gear. Next, I saw the familiar face of a young Syd Barrett. From that point on, the exhibition followed a chronological timeline, with each room highlighting another chapter or theme in Pink Floyd's history. It was like stepping into a giant time-machine. There were loads of instruments, pictures, videos, props, and memorabilia. Nothing much new under the sun, but it was a great sentimental stroll through memory lane.

It didn't really touch me emotionally until halfway through, when I spied a small Polaroid picture of a fat, bald Syd in Abbey Road. The only piece of physical evidence of one of the most remarkable stories in the history of popular music. The iconic shot was a sad reminder of a legend who had lost the spark in his eyes. I'd seen the photo before in a book or some magazine. And even then I'd found it painful to watch. Now recalling the Syd I'd met on holiday in Spain, the impact of the image was a hundred times stronger. I felt a knot in my stomach and tears welling up.

The area showing memorabilia from The Wall, including a larger than life, inflatable teacher hanging from the ceiling, was the busiest. The room with pics and props from The Final Cut was small. Unsurprisingly, the part showing Pink Floyd mark III and the slick, carefully constructed sounds and sights of A Momentary Lapse Of Reason, were decidedly different and contrasted hugely with everything that I'd seen before. Fortunately, the music improved with each step forward, and I loved hearing the warm loving words in admiration of the life and work of Richard Wright towards the end.

Still one more room to go. No headset required here. I stepped into a large 'cinema'; surrounding video walls, quadrophonic sound, moving spotlights and even some lasers, all adding to the immersive Pink Floyd experience. People were standing, sitting, and lying everywhere. Just like the good old days.

They were playing Comfortably Numb and showing shots from the mother of all reunions: Live 8. With the eyes of the world watching them one last time, all four members had finally pushed their egos aside and stood together side by side like brothers. What an appropriately way to end the exhibition.

The videos continued on loop as people entered and left the room. I decided to stay a little longer and sat down. I'd just seen fifty years of Pink Floyd pass before my eyes. I'd been watching the timeline of how they'd won the hearts of millions and millions of people. Not only across the world, but across many generations. I realised how privileged I had been.

And now it had run its course.

▪ ▪ ▪

Leaving the museum, I was greeted by the sunshine and the comforting temperature of a warm summer's day. Life carries on, I thought as I joined the rush of people and cars on the ever busy London streets. This is not the end of an era, it's a day like any other day. A perfect day to finish a book.

ACKNOWLEDGEMENTS

The author would like to thank the Pink Floyd community, fans, and journalists for helping and guiding me through the writing process. None of this would have been possible without the help of some very special people: my wife Elly (for her love & understanding), Ronen Goldman for lending me his great cover photo, my editor for her invaluable help, Jan-Maarten de Winter, Cherie van Gelder and Hans van den Heuvel (for trying to make a decent journalist out of me), Tjerk Lammers, Charles Beterams for his PF sanity check, the fine Canadian gentlemen from SAGA (who guided me through the rocky roads of the music industry), Peter Michielse for constantly trying to push me forward. And finally, the full cast of the mighty Pink Floyd for being such a great source of inspiration.

BIBLIOGRAPHY

A lot of the source material for this book is taken from interviews conducted by the author and based on his reviews of Pink Floyd and related concerts, and on his experiences as a music journalist since 1987.

Personal archive:

▪ Interviews: David Gilmour, Roger Waters, Nick Mason, and Rick Wright for several publications in OOR, Aloha, Revolver, Lust For Life, iO Pages.

▪ Concerts: Pink Floyd (1988, 1989, 1994), David Gilmour (1984, 2006), Roger Waters (1984, 2002, 2006, 2008, 2011, 2013, 2018), Nick Mason (2018).

Other important source material and inspiration for the book include:

Pink Floyd websites:

- Pinkfloyd.com
- Pinkfloyd.eu
- Rogerwaters.com
- Davidgilmour.com
- Neptunepinkfloyd.co.uk
- Brain-damage.co.uk
- Pink-floyd.org

▪ Pinkfloydz.com

Books:
▪ Echoes - The Complete History Of Pink Floyd by Glenn Povey (mindheadpublishing.co.uk)
▪ Inside Out: A Personal History Of Pink Floyd by Nick Mason (weidenfeldandnicolson.co.uk/contributor/nick-mason/)
▪ Memoirs Of The Bright Side Of The Moon by Ginger Gilmour (gingergilmour.co.uk)
▪ Pink Floyd: I Was Here by Richard Houghton (richardmhoughton.com)
▪ Pink Floyd In Nederland by Charles Beterams (permafrostpublishers.com)
▪ Pink Floyd: Their Mortal Remains by V&A Publishing (vam.ac.uk)
▪ Saucerful Of Secrets, The Pink Floyd Odyssey by Nicholas Schaffner
▪ The Rough Guide To Pink Floyd by Toby Manning
▪ In The Pink (Not a hunting memoir) by Nick Sedgwick

Magazines:
▪ Classic Rock - 30 Years On.. Pink Floyd, The World Behind The Wall by Glenn Povey, Jann Uhelszki & Kevin Murphy, 2009
▪ History Of Rock (Melody Maker) - 1980 - Roger Hates Everything by Michael Watts
▪ Mojo Magazine - Welcome To My Nightmare by David Fricke & Behind The Wall by Mark Blake, 2009
▪ Mojo Magazine - Pink Floyd 1965 - 1973, The Collectors' Series, 2019
▪ Prog Magazine - A Hole In The Wall by Marcel Anders, 2017
▪ Rolling Stone - Back To The Wall by Brian Hiatt, 2010

▪ Rolling Stone - Pink Floyd, Special Collector's Edition, 2017
▪ Uncut - Coming Back To Life... by Michael Bonner, 2014
▪ Uncut - We're All In This Together by Michael Bonner, 2017

Online articles:
▪ BBC News - Did Live 8 make a difference? by Ian Youngs, 2006
▪ Beat Instrumental - Guitarist Of The Month: Syd Barrett, 1967
▪ Brain Damage - Wray Ellis
▪ Brain Damage - Richard Ashton and Glenn Povey, 1987
▪ Chris Charlesworth, 1974
▪ Classic Rock - 50 Years Of Pink Floyd: A Most Unlikely Reunion, by Johnny Black, 2015
▪ Creem Magazine - The Sun Is Eclipsed By The Moon, 1988
▪ Daily Mirror, by Ros Wynne-Jones, 2003
▪ Daily Telegraph - Roger Waters: Rebel Without A Pause, 2000
▪ Daily Telegraph - The Other Side Of The Moon, 2002
▪ EMI interview by Mark Blake, 1996
▪ Exit - Nick Mason interviewed in Hungary, 2006
▪ Fox News - Backstage in London: An 'A' for Live 8 by Roger Friedman, 2005
▪ Humo - Where Are They Now by Serge Simonart, 2005
▪ Galore Magazine - Rock stars have to show off because they've got weak egos, 2005
▪ Great Music Stories - Snowy White - The Pink Floyd & Thin Lizzy Years, 2017
▪ Guardian Newspaper, 2002
▪ Guitar Classics VI - Out of the Pink and into the Blues: David Gilmour by John Stix, 1985
▪ Guitar World - Careful With That Axe by Lenny Baker, 1993
▪ Guitar World - Sound of Silence by Brad Tolinski, 1994

▪ In Rock - Interview with Snowy White by Alexander Zheleznov and Dasha Dykhanovska, 2011
▪ Independent - Roger Waters: Pink Floyd star on why his fellow musicians are terrified to speak out against Israel by Paul Gallager, 2013
▪ Newshub.co.nz - Inside David Gilmour's Astoria houseboat recording studio, 2008
▪ Interview Magazine - The Colour Of Floyd by Graham Fuller, 1994
▪ KulturSpiegel - Rock music is no nuclear physics by Simon Rosenberg, 2006
▪ Los Angeles Times - Dark Side of The Tube by Richard Cromelin, 1992
▪ Mail Online - The dark side of Pink Floyd by Angella Johnson, 2016
▪ Melody Maker - The Great Pink Floyd Mystery by Chris Welch, 1967
▪ Melody Maker - Hits? The Floyd Couldn't Care Less by Alan Walsh, 1967
▪ Melody Maker - Troubled Waters by Michael Watts, 1970
▪ Mojo Magazine - The Third Coming, 1994
▪ Mojo Magazine - The 30 Year Technicolour Dream, 1995
▪ Mojo Magazine - Danger! Demolition in Progress, 1999
▪ Mojo Magazine, 2001
▪ Mojo Magazine, 2003
▪ MTV - Backstage At Live 8: Bono Works The Crowd, Jay-Z Keeps Cool by Bob Mancini, 2005
▪ Musician Magazine - Careful With That Axe by David Fricke, 1982
▪ Musician Magazine, Repent, Pink Floyd Idolaters!, 1988
▪ New Indian Express, 2002

▪ NME News desk, 2015
▪ Penthouse Magazine, 1988
▪ Peter Watts interview by Frank Torker, 1973
▪ Phil Taylor and The Astoria; Driving Audio Standards on the River Thames by Jeff Touzeau, 2005
▪ Q Magazine - Over The Wall, An Interview With Roger Waters by Chris Salewicz, 1987
▪ Q Magazine - The rightful heir?, 1990
▪ Q Magazine - Here We Go, Here We Go, Here We Go, 1994
▪ Record Collector - David Gilmour Interview by Daryl Easlea, 2003
▪ Rock Compact Disc magazine, 1992
▪ Rolling Stone - Pink Floyd: The Inside Story by David Fricke, 1987
▪ Rolling Stone - Kory Grow, 2014
▪ Rolling Stone - Pink Floyd Reunited With Roger Waters 10 Years Ago This Week by Andy Greene, 2015
▪ Rolling Stone - David Gilmour on Pink Floyd: It's a Shame, but This Is the End by Daniel Kreps, 2014
▪ Rolling Stone - Nick Mason on the State of Pink Floyd: It's Silly to Still Be Fighting by Andy Greene, 2018
▪ Seven days, An Interview On The Dark Side by Moody Kriteman, 1996
▪ Sounds Guitar Heroes magazine - The Rise of Pink Floyd and the Decline of Syd Barrett, 1983
▪ Spin - Remembering Roger Waters' 1990 Concert at the Berlin Wall by Bob Guccione, 2017
▪ Sunday Times - Hunter Davies column, 1966
▪ 50 Years Of Pink Floyd: A Most Unlikely Reunion by Johnny Black, 2018

▪ The Age, Not Just Another Brick In The Wall by Everett True, 2002
▪ The Austin Chronicle - Pink Floyd's Roger Waters Gets Political With the Chronicle by Raoul Hernandez, 2020
▪ The Guardian - The Floyd's tour de force by Robin Denselow, 1988
▪ The Guardian - Roger Waters: I'm prepared to be wrong about everything by Alexis Petridis, 2015
▪ The Guardian - David Gilmour: I've been bonded to Charlie since he was three. We were incensed by the injustice by Ginny Dougary, 2016
▪ The Guardian - If you believe in human rights, Madonna, don't play Tel Aviv by Roger Waters, 2019
▪ The Mail On Sunday - Angella Johnson, 2016
▪ The Source - Shades Of Pink, US radio, 1984
▪ The Telegraph - David Gilmour: A Pink Floyd reunion? Impossible by Neil McCormick, 2015
▪ The Telegraph: Hay Festival 2016: David Gilmour and Polly Samson talk marriage, making music and the trouble with Pink Floyd, by Helen Brown, 2016
▪ The Telegraph - Pink Floyd's Roger Waters: 'Dave Gilmour and I will never be mates' by Neil McCormick, 2017
▪ The Tribune - The Different Shades Of Roger Waters by G. Kot, 1999
▪ Time Magazine - Music: Pooh-bahs of Poverty by Josh Tyrangiel, 2005
▪ Toronto Sun, 1996
▪ Uncut - Lost In Space, 2003
▪ Uncut - The Final Cut interview by Carol Clerk, 2004
▪ Uncut - Set The Controls For The Heart Of The Floyd, 2007
▪ Washington Post - One Giant Step for Pink Floyd, 1992

- Word Magazine - No Pain No Gain by Mark Ellen, 2008
- Yedioth Ahronoth - Interview with Roger Waters by Alon Hadar, 2016
- Zigzag, 1973

Online video & audio:

- Australian radio, 1988
- BBC Radio 1, The Wall album, interviewed by Tommy Vance, 1979
- BBC Radio 2, 2002
- BBC - David Gilmour: Wider Horizons by Lesley Douglas, Alan Yentob, Kieran Evans and Sara Martin, 2016
- Capital Radio - Pink Floyd Story, 1976/1977
- David Gilmour: Wider Horizons by BBC, 2015
- Howard Stern - interview with Roger Waters, 2012
- Huffington Post live - interview with Roger Waters
- Scottish TV interview David Gilmour, 2006
- SFX Radio Show - Roger Waters interview by Jim Ladd, 2000
- The Andrew Marr Show, 2015

DVD's:

- Classic Albums - Pink Floyd, The Making Of The Dark Side Of The Moon, 2003
- Pink Floyd: The Story Of Wish You Were Here, 2011

Other:

- A funny joke by Gary Kemp, 2018 (on stage in Amsterdam)
- Ozark, Season 2, Episode 6, Netflix, 2019
- The Pink Floyd Exhibition: Their Mortal Remains, Victoria & Albert Museum, London

ABOUT THE AUTHOR

Edwin Ammerlaan began as a music journalist for OOR magazine in 1986. Since then, he has interviewed over 300 musicians and bands and his articles have appeared in various Dutch music publications including Revolver, Lust For Life, Aloha and iO Pages. He is also the author of 'SAGA, The Biography' (2010). Edwin Ammerlaan lives in Amsterdam, The Netherlands.

Printed in Great Britain
by Amazon

56141632R00142